# Saving
# the seed

# About GRAIN

GRAIN (Genetic Resources Action International), a non-profit, non-governmental organisation, has long been active in the issues surrounding global management and control of plant genetic resources. While most of GRAIN's work is focused on the developing countries, genetic resources and local development are critical concerns in the North as well. Since 1988, 'Conservation in Europe' has been an integral component of GRAIN's agenda for action within the NGO community. Most of GRAIN's work is devoted to raising public awareness and stimulating alternatives to combat both genetic erosion and increasing monopoly control over the first link in the food chain, through networking, lobbying, and information activities at the international level.

For more information about how to get involved, please contact:

GRAIN
Jonqueres 16, 6-D
E-08003 Barcelona
Spain
Tel: (34-3) 310 59 09
Fax: (34-3) 310 59 52
E-mail: GEO2: GRAIN

# Saving
# the seed

Genetic diversity and European agriculture

Renée Vellvé

EARTHSCAN

Earthscan Publications Ltd, London

First published 1992 by
Earthscan Publications Limited
120 Pentonville Road, London N1 9JN

Copyright © GRAIN, 1992

British Library Cataloguing-in-Publication Data

A catalogue record for this book is available from the British Library

ISBN 1 85383 1506

Typeset by Books Unlimited (Nottm) – Sutton-in-Ashfield, NG17 1AL
Printed by Biddles Ltd, Guildford and Kings Lynn.

Earthscan Publications Ltd is an editorially independent subsidiary of Kogan
Page Ltd and publishes in association with the International Institute for
Environment and Development and the World Wide Fund for Nature.

# Contents

**ANNEXES:**

# Tables, graphs and boxes

# List of acronyms

| | |
|---|---|
| CAP | Common Agricultural Policy (EEC) |
| CGIAR | Consulative Group on International Agricultural Research |
| CMS | cytoplasmic male sterility |
| COMECON | Council for Mutual Economic Aid |
| DNA | deoxyribonucleic acid |
| DUS | 'distinct', 'uniform', 'stable' |
| EC | European Community |
| ECU | European Currency Unit |
| EEC | European Economic Community |
| EUCARPIA | European Association for Plant Breeding Research |
| FAO | Food and Agriculture Organisation |
| GATT | General Agreement on Tarrifs and Trade |
| HDRA | Hendry Doubleday Research Association, UK |
| IARCs | International Agricultural Research Centres (CGIAR) |
| IBPGR | International Board for Plant Genetic Resources (CGIAR) |
| INRA | Institut National de la Recherche Agronomique, France |
| IPOs | Intellectual Property Obligations |
| NGOs | non-governmental organisations |
| ONIC | Office National Interprofessionel des Céréales, France |
| PAGE PACA | Patrimoine Génétique de Provence-Alpes-Côtes d'Azur, France |
| PBR | Plant Breeders' Rights |
| PGR | plant genetic resources |
| PR | public relations |
| SADCC | South African Development Cooperation Conference |
| TAC | Technical Advisory Committee (CGIAR) |
| UN | United Nations |
| UNCED | United Nations Conference on Environment and Development |
| UPOV | Union for the Protection of New Varieties of Plants |

# About this book

The global nature of issues like biodiversity, tropical forests and climate change should not blur the fact that we all have to get our own houses in order. And in Europe, our house is in pretty bad shape. The environmental and social costs of our industrialised food system are becoming untenable in both the short and long term, and people – from consumers to policy-makers – are trying to find new ways around it. Genetic resources are at the heart of this problem. The vulnerability of our plants and animals, who controls conservation and breeding, what kind of choices people have in growing crops and raising livestock, are some of the questions we need to look at more seriously. At stake is the integrity of the food system upon which we all depend.

For as long as there have been farmers and gardeners, saving seeds has been an essential part of survival. It still is. The problem is that people have been progressively stripped of this role, while our governments hardly do a good job of conserving what are in fact our only options for tomorrow. If we are to face the challenge of adapting food production to pressures like new pests and disease, climate change or the requirements of sustainable agriculture, then we need to have access to a broad range of varieties suited to different needs. Current neglect for conserving those resources must be turned around and people's role in using and maintaining a broad spectrum of locally-adapted varieties reasserted. In this book, we focus on people's control of the genetic base of crop agriculture, a heritage developed by generations of farming and gardening families throughout Europe. But obviously, the question of developing a more sustainable agriculture, integrated with environmental, social and political concerns, is a much broader one.

In taking this effort to print, our thanks go first of all to the people working unasked and unnoticed throughout the regions of Europe, on their farms and in their gardens, to save diverse breeds and seeds against the onslaught of uniformity. The few people we highlight in this book have shared a lot with us, and in the process have taught us quite a bit. We are grateful to each of them: Nancy Arrowsmith, Philippe Barret, Martin Bossart and Peter Raatsie, Giovanni Cerretelli and Francesca Castioni, Jeremy Cherfas, Hans-Peter Grünenfelder, Thomas Levander, Gus Lieberwerth, Jürgen Reckin and Sylvia Schmid.

We would also like to thank the people from Europe's genebank community – national coordinators and active scientists, too many to name – who provided information, personal perspectives and a better idea of the

9

pressures they are up against. In particular we want to express our sincere appreciation to Jaap Hardon, who has done more than any other genebank director to try to wrest support for long-term conservation of genetic diversity in Europe, recognising that amateurs and NGOs have a critical role to play. Also, IBPGR staffers Pierre Perret and Mark Perry deserve acknowledgement for their generosity in handing over documentation and databases at all too numerous requests.

The editing of the drafts was taken up by close colleagues long committed to grassroots conservation and use of genetic diversity as a necessary approach to local agricultural development. Henk Hobbelink, coordinator of GRAIN, took on the unenviable challenge of turning a chaotic manuscript into something readable. Jeremy Cherfas meticulously turned the English into real English and garble into logic, while Michael Flitner, Hannes Lorenzen and Michel Pimbert made critical improvements on the arguments. These people pushed and pulled the book to its delivery.

Finally, the research, writing and production of this book would not have been possible without the financial support of those agencies which have funded GRAIN's programme over the years, of which this publication is an integral part: Catholic Fund for Overseas Development (UK), CS Fund (USA), Danchurchaid (Denmark), Dutch Ministry of Development Cooperation, Misereor (Germany), Norwegian Ministry of Environment, Novib (Netherlands), Swedish International Development Authority, Swissaid (Switzerland), Trócaire (Ireland).

Renée Vellvé
GRAIN
Barcelona, August 1992

# Foreword

This book reflects a growing concern that in modern agriculture people are losing control over genetic diversity and the crops and varieties they grow. It analyses what is being done in Europe to safeguard genetic diversity at the levels of citizens, governments and industry. It concludes that industry, supported by government action, increasingly controls genetic diversity and its use. It highlights what concerned citizens consider to be mismanagement of genetic diversity as a cultural heritage by the modern industrial complex. Increased uniformity in farmers' fields is furthermore seen as a threat to sustainability and a threat to the rights of people who created diversity in the first place – farmers and gardeners.

The issues are well researched, giving evidence of a growing professionalism in non-governmental organisations concerned with the conservation and use of biodiversity. The book questions developments that seem intent on limiting – if not prohibiting – the involvement of ordinary people at the grassroots level in this important endeavour.

The formal institutional and industrial complex must take notice of these views. It must recognise the fact that genetic diversity serves more interests than just those of industrial agriculture. In Western Europe, our record in conserving genetic diversity is modest to say the least. There are few regions in the world other than Europe where so much original landrace material has been lost through failure of both institutional and private plant breeders to accept broad responsibility for conserving such materials when replaced by modern varieties beyond the immediate requirements of on-going breeding programmes. Even today, and in spite of Europe's reasonably progressive attitude at the UN Conference on Environment and Development (UNCED 1992) where biodiversity was high on the agenda, genetic resources conservation in Europe continues to receive only marginal attention in the formal sector. Combined with the massive standardisation of our food system, this lack of priority has destroyed more diversity in the past few decades here than ever before.

In the chapter aptly entitled 'Salvaging in Silence', actions undertaken by local non-governmental organisations in Europe to conserve and use

11

old varieties are reviewed. Many of these groups found themselves up against a powerful industry intent on regulating the seed market. This was partly done to protect the interests of farmers and ensure the quality and identity of seeds offered for sale. However, at the same time, Plant Breeders' Rights and national varietal lists, strengthened by EC legislation establishing the Common Catalogue of varieties, actually outlawed conservation and use of local varieties at the grassroots level. In spite of this, concerned NGOs in many countries took it upon themselves to collect and save old varieties, to make them available to farmers and gardeners interested in more than just high yields. The argument is clear. For certain, plant breeding needs to be regulated in the interest of farmers, as a form of consumer protection. However, the present bias towards stimulating and protecting the commercial interests of plant breeding needs to be rectified. It must leave room for alternative approaches and options for farmers and gardeners, and at the same time stimulate the use of genetic diversity rather than restrict it.

While this book deals essentially with the situation in Europe, inferences to the developing countries are clear. The same mistakes should be avoided.

The formal genetic resources system, linking *ex situ* genebanks with institutional and private plant breeding, and ultimately farmers, is mainly relevant to those conditions where modern varieties are adopted or for those crops covered by formal plant breeding. It leaves out farmers and gardeners who rely on landraces and on-farm crop improvement and seed production. While this group may be relatively small in industrialised countries, in developing countries this is by far the large majority and includes farmers in most centres of diversity of our crops – farmers who are custodians of much of the genetic diversity that still exists.

There are numerous examples of minor crops and even major crops for limited, often more marginal and diverse, environments that will not justify – for economic reasons – costly, separate institutional breeding programmes. Under these conditions, many farmers will continue to rely on local on-farm crop improvement and seed production. This informal system should be recognised as having its own merits complementing the institutional system. It should not, as appears to be the case at present in Western Europe, be restricted by seed legislation and adverse agricultural policies.

This book provides a strong statement critical of the institutional system. Even if one does not agree with all that is said, it does suggest that there is some imbalance in the formal system that must be adjusted.

Higher productivity is essential to feed a growing world population and institutional and private plant breeding have an important role to play. However, this should not be achieved at the expense of a range of other approaches by monopolising the mandate to preserve and exploit genetic diversity.

This book deserves a wide audience. It may stimulate all those concerned with the conservation and use of genetic diversity to take a broader view. It may be particularly relevant to those in government and the Commission of the European Community who seem to have difficulty in grasping the importance of genetic conservation – and the need for joint action – in spite of the political support generated by the European Parliament for an integrated conservation strategy for the EC. Europe simply cannot afford to lag behind in contributing to the conservation of plant genetic resources if we want to maintain our access to such diversity for our future food production. The message of the book is that we need to do so in a manner whereby citizens, governments and industry alike participate in complementary and even cooperative programmes. It provides constructive suggestions to develop such activities within the context of agricultural policies, legal frameworks and research agendas. Europe can and should take the lead in coordinated action and in providing a policy platform recognising biodiversity, and genetic resources in particular, as a global resource implying global responsibility to manage it. Time is running out. The alternative is a race to satisfy immediate needs of plant breeding and biotechnology at the expense of future options and unabated genetic erosion.

Jaap Hardon
Director
Centre for Genetic Resources, The Netherlands
Wageningen, June 1992

# Introduction

If you stop and ask anyone walking down the street what 'genetic erosion' is, you are likely to get some furrowed brows as a response. To most people, 'genetic' has something to do with biology and those microscopic things called genes, while 'erosion' is what happens to soils and coastlines when they are washed or blown away. How on earth could genes get blown away? Yet if you go on to ask if anyone remembers something about an old and tasty apple or tomato that is nowhere to be found in the supermarkets any more, yes, that does ring a bell. What could these two questions possibly have to do with each other and why should anyone care?

Genetic erosion is in fact something like genes getting blown away – it is a violent process of replacing diversity with uniformity. Where diversity means choice, contrasts, options, alternatives and competition, uniformity means sameness, dullness, limits, dictatorships and monopolies. And the problem is not just genetic. As we destroy the resources necessary for crop production – be it our water, soils, climate or plants – we are losing the means to take decisions tomorrow as to how we organise ourselves as societies. And as we passively sit and watch a few mega-corporations, like Ciba-Geigy or Sandoz, turn our farms into factories and claim patent rights on plants and animals and the technologies to manipulate them, we are ceding to them control of the food chain and the life support systems that sustain us. In that sense, this book is definitely not about ecology. It's not even about plants, although it talks a lot about them. It is about people and the political responsibilities we have to keep options – diversity – alive.

## Seeds of survival

Despite the tens of millions of plant species that exist, we depend on no more than thirty or so to feed us. Of those thirty, three cereals alone – rice, maize and wheat – provide the basis of what most people eat each day. Our survival ultimately depends on theirs and vice-versa. One 'perfect' type of lettuce or barley will never be enough to supply a region or a country with the salad and animal feed it needs year after year. Plants

**14**

have to evolve or they die. They cannot evolve without other plants to provide useful genes to fend off a new virus or withstand longer periods of drought as weather patterns change. In other words, plants depend on the availability of genetic diversity and that depends on us.

Plants are also an important part of our cultural survival. The crops we grow did not fall out of the sky. They are a living heritage. Generation after generation, people have been tailoring plants, watching them, learning from them and passing the good results on. Be it a certain potato that could withstand late spring frosts in Sweden or a radish that wasn't so sharp that a Spaniard would find it inedible, gardeners and farming families have created, hands-on, an incredible panorama of different crop varieties to suit their needs, customs and tastes. And in so doing they lay their story down and give that story a name, often suggesting the plant's origin or qualities. Just as stories have to be told, plants have to be reproduced – or they simply fade out of existence.

## Conservation consciousness

Pandas are cute, tropical rainforests are breath-taking, but how do you mobilise people to save a carrot? It is extremely difficult unless they see and feel what is at stake. But often enough, that doesn't happen until it is too late. It was all too easy for one single fungus to wipe out Ireland's potato harvest in the 1840s, the staple food at the time, because everyone was growing a susceptible variety. Millions of people died and countless others fled the country in search of food and a livelihood. Before and since, similar scenarios have struck other crops in other lands and afflicted other peoples the world over. The message is staring us in the face: uniformity spells big risks and we are responsible for it.

In European agriculture, farmers are growing fewer crops. Of those crops, they are sowing fewer varieties. And within those varieties there is very little . . . variety! Not too long ago, most farmers were breeders themselves, experimenting, choosing, crossing, selecting and saving seeds for the next growing season. With the industrialisation of agriculture, people have lost that fundamental capacity to choose, create and control the basis of food production. It has been silently hijacked by those who are turning agri-'culture' into agri-'business' and farmers into assembly line workers. As industry replaces agriculture, so a handful of new, genetically similar 'super seeds' replaces the broad diversity of locally adapted farmer-saved seeds.

The problem is that we cannot create new seeds without the old ones. And we don't know what we will want or need tomorrow. Each variety

**15**

of turnip, squash, wheat or olive that disappears means the irreplaceable loss of part of our past and part of our future. We simply cannot tell when another virus or fungus or change in the weather will bring about the loss of who knows how many hectares of farmland sown to the same uniform seeds. Under these circumstances, genetic conservation is not a consideration, it is an imperative.

## Of rights and responsibilities

In the 1960s, the scientific community woke up to the dramatic plague of genetic erosion in the world's most important regions of biological diversity: the farmers' fields of Asia, Africa and Latin America. This was where most of our crops originated and diversified. And this is where the key sources of genes for future food production lie. As an emergency response, seed stores called 'genebanks' were built and collecting missions were mounted to rescue what was still left in the fields and put it in what was meant to be safe keeping for tomorrow.

In the 1970s, politicians and citizens' groups the world over realised just how fast the agrochemical industry of Europe and North America had taken over control of the seed supply, and with it the first link in the food chain. The chemical bias in breeding and farmers' loss of control over their production systems was leading to greater dependency and less sustainability. Worse, though, was the news that the companies were claiming and getting private monopoly rights over those seeds, in the form of Plant Breeders' Rights (PBR), despite the fact that farmers had put more sweat into developing the raw materials than any corporate lab technician putting on the finishing touches.

In the 1980s, it became increasingly evident that the genebank system was terribly skewed. Technically, it left a lot to be desired, as many seeds were dying in storage. Politically, it was under the control of too few desires, namely those of the rich North. At the same time, industry, increasingly fascinated by the glitter and profits to be reaped from the new biotechnologies, began lobbying for even more potent forms of monopoly rights over plants. PBR was not enough; only real patents could guarantee stronger control over markets and farmers.

As we enter the 1990s it is clear that governments and industry are doing more to create the problem than to construct the solutions. Governments use their right to destroy genetic diversity in whatever way possible. Industry claims the right legally to own whatever is left. What about people, the farmers, gardeners and consumers who created that diversity in the first place? What rights do they have? Basically none, not even the right to assume the responsibility for managing that diversity at a down-to-earth level, where it can be used and enjoyed, where it can flourish.

This book is part of the fight for that right: the right of local organisations and motivated people to regain control over plant genetic diversity and use it to build a more sustainable future. Without it, development will be meaningless and global food security ill assured – even in Europe. The price we are paying for the genetic uniformity of our agriculture – which translates into escalating chemical bills, soil erosion, water pollution and farmers' dependency on industry – is all too high.

For the past couple of years, GRAIN has been looking closely at who is doing what in Europe to safeguard genetic diversity at all the different levels: citizens, governments and industry. Frankly, we are alarmed. Not so much by what has been lost already – it is not our point to mourn and grieve – but by the lack of seriousness and responsibility our governments are taking towards genetic resources management and the violent forces that are prohibiting ordinary people from participating in that vital endeavour at the grassroots level. Somehow, this state of affairs must be rapidly turned around.

This journey through the birth, decline and current mismanagement of our crop heritage in Europe shows us one important thing: that people have to regain their key position as the starting point for conservation and production. It is one thing to come to grips with the failings of our government efforts to store our genetic wealth for future needs. But it is quite another thing to discover that, against all tides, there are indeed a number of people out there taking into their own hands the imperative to use and maintain our crop heritage alive. These people are not cultivating museums, as many of their governments are. Moved by the loss of what are valuable plants, they are managing diversity in day to day gardening and farming: growing it, nurturing it, working with it and enjoying it. In so doing, they are preserving what are in fact our options for tomorrow: ours as ordinary people, not as governments, with the responsibility to design a more sustainable food system.

The farmers, gardeners and citizens' groups contributing to this unknown effort in Europe are salvaging both our past and our future in silence. Their work goes unseen, unrecognised, unsupported and unvalued. Picking up the work where the official sector is going wrong, they are the hidden but fundamental cornerstone of securing a better future for agriculture, one which doesn't just exploit but maintains and rebuilds constantly. Bringing conservation back into production and actively supporting such hands-on work with genetic diversity at the grassroots level are becoming more urgent than ever.

# 1: The making of a heritage

*Today's gardeners cannot possibly comprehend the amount of history contained in their seeds, both what has come before and what may potentially come after their brief involvement.*

Suzanne Ashworth, seed saver, 1991[1]

To some, genetic diversity is a 'genepool', an immense supply of raw materials to be tapped for making crops grow, like the oil wells of Saudi Arabia make cars run. To others, it is the full spectrum of all that is different, unique, vast and interesting; the range between yellow and black potatoes. To yet others, it is a living history of what their grandparents and great grandparents grew, either on the same plot of land or half a world away. Actually, genetic diversity is all of these things at once: a moving mixture of the past and the future, a source of wealth and fertility, a coloured tableau of nature's possibilities and culture's limits. It would seem impossible to adopt one single attitude towards the complexity of life forms and forces surrounding us. Diversity simply has no face value. Depending on whatever aspect moves you most about it, you can be nostalgic, intellectual, scientific, spiritual, profit-hungry, or simply concerned about survival.

At the bottom line, when we confront the spread and depth of the diversity of plants that have fed, housed, clothed and cured people all through our existence, we cannot escape that awesome confrontation with time and space. Over an unimaginable number of years plants have evolved and co-evolved with the people who used them; their history and ours, their destiny and ours are intertwined. The open-ended array of soils they have grown in, the hands they have been cared for by, and values they have been fashioned to serve – the diversity of our crop plants is a direct reflection of the diversity of our cultures.

One way we like to look at it is to call it a heritage. That is a word loaded with all sorts of legal, political and ethical implications. But it is also a simple and powerful one. The ancient Romans called it *patrimonium*, from *pater* (father). It was used to designate that which was inherited from your father to be transmitted to the next generation, a chain of transmission that could not be interrupted. It was used precisely to distinguish between those goods that could be exchanged for their current monetary value, and those things that had a deeper, inalienable family and community value.

Plants definitely fall into this category, although maybe we should rename it *matrimonium*, since in many societies throughout history saving seeds, nurturing wild plants and breeding new crop varieties was largely carried out by women. Plants are a fundamental part of the chain of life that keeps this planet going and the diversity within them is the key to their survival. Some of that diversity has evolved through the changing pressures of the environment, but much of it is the result of continuous generations of people tampering with it and passing it on. We will never be able to measure how much credit goes to 'either side', but there is certainly a part of both. In this sense, genetic diversity is both a natural and cultural heritage that *has to* be transmitted for the sake of survival. Calling genetic diversity a heritage is not only recognising the role plants play in the chain of life, but also opens up the question as to who is responsible for keeping that chain intact and extending it.

## Taming the wild

People were not always farmers and gardeners. Agriculture, in fact, is a rather modern enterprise. Only about ten to fifteen thousand years ago did people start settling down and figuring out new ways to control their food supply. Before then, men and women sustained themselves and their families through gathering, hunting and fishing. Ten to fifteen thousand years might seem a long time ago, but if you consider that there have been people on this planet for perhaps five million years, it's clear that agriculture was historically invented yesterday.

Most of our ancestors did not bother 'growing' plants. They picked them from their surroundings: berries, grains, vegetables, nuts and roots. Food was abundant and populations were small. Many people were nomads, roaming at their own pace to and from areas particularly rich in plant and animal diversity. Others were more sedentary fisherfolk, living on seafood and the plants that grew near watershores, estuaries and riverbanks. The move to settle down and take on the quite different task of cultivating plants did not happen overnight. It must have been a gradual process that probably took place at more or less the same time in various parts of the world: China and southeast Asia, the Middle East, the Andes and parts of Africa. In the wetter tropical zones of Asia and Latin America, the first crops to be domesticated were probably roots and tubers, such as yams or potatoes. In the arid and semi-arid regions, like southwest Asia, cereals such as barley were probably the first food crop grown.

The logic of cultivating plants around a village or settlement was in most cases probably not driven by hunger. Nor did crop cultivation totally replace the art of gathering, which remained, and still remains today, a source of food for many people. At the same time, it should be recognised that not every society has taken on sowing or hoeing at all. Various groups in Australia, Africa and the Americas still get by hunting and collecting food.

Many of the plants that people first went out of their way to nurture were useful for specific needs: religious and social ceremonies; painting, dyeing, weaving; making tools, containers and utensils; constructing fences or houses; making medicine, poison, beverages or cosmetics; extracting oils, providing animal feed, and so on. In fact, plants that could fulfil more than one purpose probably received more attention than others. Sorghum was grown early on in Africa to provide not just the dinner meal but also forage for animals, syrup for drinks, stalks to make brooms, popping seed for amusing snacks and flower heads for ornamental decorations[2]. Cannabis, or hemp, was one of the first crops people cultivated in Eurasia. When it reached China around 2500 BC it was used for fibre, before its narcotic properties were exploited in India later on[3]. Over in Brazil, manioc (or cassava) was used to provide toxins to poison arrowheads for game hunting and to kill fish in streams before people figured out how to detoxify it and cook it[4]. In Europe, many of the cereals we grow for bread or fodder today were first venerated as sacred plants associated with the gods Demeter and Ceres, and had a primary role in medicine[5].

But nurturing a plant is not the same thing as domesticating it. Many plants are 'cultivated' without being fully 'domesticated'. They may be weeds, wild plants, or crops undergoing adaptation towards domestication. They may be simply tolerated, actively protected or actually sown and harvested. Small-scale farmers and household gardeners 'work with' wild and semi-domesticated plants in many ways, even today. Truly domesticated plants are those that have been so severely pressured and harnessed to fit a habitat and production system, that many of them could not survive outside of that context. For example, maize and triticale are generally considered human creations. No wild form of maize has ever been found, although perennial relatives exist in Mexico, and the crop is dependent upon people to survive. Triticale is a forced combination of rye and wheat, that probably never would have crossed in nature.

In fact, while all of our crops were developed from wild plants, most passed through the phase of being a weed before they were harnessed as a crop. Rice was probably a weed in the flooded taro fields of southeast Asia before it was domesticated and grown for its nourishing grain. Wild oats were introduced into Africa and the Mediterranean as a weed associated with other cereals before they were harnessed for food and fodder. The same holds for rye in Central Europe. Potatoes, carrots and onions all have weed forms that occupy territories where there is little competition.

The differences between wild and domesticated forms of crops are often spectacular. By selecting plants and improving them through cropping techniques, farmers and gardeners have forced evolution and brought on radical changes in plants. One thing they did was focus their attention on the big and beautiful, enhancing that part of the plant that interested them most. For example, wild sunflowers look like overgrown daisies while the cultivated types we know of have the huge 'faces' loaded with rich seeds for oil or eating. Another thing they did was diversify the crop. Potatoes were selected to produce a vast range of different shaped and coloured tubers. By contrast, wild potatoes are almost invariably small, brown and nearly identical looking[6].

But perhaps most important, for the sake of being able to grow crops on any reasonable scale, people overcame two important characteristics that are typical of wild species. The first is the tendency of wild plants to 'shatter', whereby mature fruits and seeds are released very easily into the wind or onto the ground to propagate further individuals. This is great for ensuring the plant's survival through scattered dissemination, but a nightmare for someone who wants to fill a basket and harvest the goods. So farmers had to select carefully those plants that shattered least and keep selecting and multiplying them until they could stabilise a crop that did not fall apart on them any more.

The second major characteristic of wild plants that had to be tamed for rational cultivation was their tendency to germinate erratically. This makes it easier for some individual plants to succeed and grow if others get wiped out by cold or drought, but results in a very uneven harvest. Again, selective pressures brought these irregular germination rates under some form of control. There is a whole range of other characteristics that people focused on when harnessing wild plants for crop production. Together, they make up what is called the domestication syndrome or complex.

But domestication, a big step in itself, was only the striking of the match that unleashed a veritable fire of crop diversification and the development of agriculture. Ever since you could rightly call a farmer a farmer, or a gardener a gardener, people have been choosing, selecting, fashioning and creating a tremendous array of different varieties of crops to suit different needs and fancies. They may not have known what 'genes' were, but they certainly took tremendous advantage of the versatility of plants and their capacity to adapt to a very wide range of environments, climates and cultures.

## The geography of diversity

Agriculture was introduced into Europe sometime around 3–4,000 BC, as waves of migrants came in from Anatolia and the Middle East through to Central Europe, and from North Africa up the Iberian peninsula and into France and southern England. These people brought with them their ingenuity and know-how in, among other things, constructing tools, making pottery, raising livestock and cultivating crops. Later, the Mediterranean coastline was colonised from the east by people practising the earliest farming systems we know of in Europe, revolving around barley, sheep and goats. Wheat and rye are also early grains that were introduced into central and northern Europe from the Mediterranean southeast.

Just as agriculture was imported into Europe, so were most of the crops we have ever grown here. Many of our cereals come from the Middle East and southwest Asia, and most of our fruits from as far away as China. Very few vegetables are actually indigenous to Europe: lettuce, onions and asparagus figure among them *(see Table 1.1)*. In fact, the history of agriculture and the history of crop evolution shows that farming spread out from just a few regions of the world, often areas where crop diversity is really intense. Not that the two always coincide. Crops have been travelling as long as people have, whether they were conquering lands, fleeing wars or simply out exploring.

As far as we know, the systematic tracking down of the origin of our

**Table 1.1:** Origins of Western Europe's vegetables

**Grown in Western Europe since prehistoric times:**
> Turnips, certain non-heading cabbages, faba bean, lentils and peas.

**Arrivals during the Greco-Roman times:**
> Large radish, melons, cucumbers, gourds, onions, chard, parsnip, carrots and black-eyed peas (cowpea).

**Introduced by Arabs and Jews between the 10th and 15th centuries:**
> Aubergine, cauliflower, watermelon, spinach, artichoke and okra.

**Brought over from the Americas after 1492:**
> Tomato, potatoes, sweet potato, common beans, squashes and peppers.

**From Asia:**
> Certain vegetables were already introduced through the Arabs while others couldn't adapt to our climates; the Japanese artichoke, yam, asparagus-lettuce and Chinese cabbage did not arrive until the 19th and 20th centuries.

**Vegetables developed or improved in Italy:**
> Bitter chicories, lettuces, head cabbage, Milan cabbage, cauliflowers and broccoli, radishes, fennel and beet.

**Vegetables that came from central and northern Europe:**
> Horseradish, rutabaga (or swede turnip), angelica and watercress.

**Recently developed vegetables:**
> Corn salad (17th c.), Brussels sprouts (18th c.), dandelion (19th c.) and endive (19th c.).

*Source:* Michel Chauvet, 'L'histoire des légumes' in *La diversité des plantes légumières: hier, aujourd'hui et demain*, JATBA, Paris, 1986, p. 10.

crops is a 19th century phenomenon. Alexander von Humboldt was probably the first to write about it in his *Essay on the Geography of Plants*, published in 1807. He said:

*The origin, the first home of the plants most useful to man and which have accompanied him from remotest epochs, is a secret as impenetrable as the dwellings of all our domestic animals. We do not know what region produced spontaneously wheat, barley, oats and rye. The plants which constitute the natural riches of all inhabitants of the tropics, the banana, the pawpaw, the cassava, and maize have never been found in wild state'.*

Von Humboldt's pessimistic curiosity was followed later on by several studies by the Swiss botanist Alphonse de Candolle, including his book *The Origin of Cultivated Plants* (1882). De Candolle, using botany, linguistics and archaeology, reasoned that our crops were probably domesticated in a few areas: China, tropical Asia, southwest Asia and Egypt.

This scholarly interest in geobotany, prevalent in the days of Darwin, gave rise to yet another concern towards the end of the century: the value of the world's crop diversity for plant breeding and the need to conserve these resources. Two German scientists – Emanuel Ritter von Proskowetz and Franz Schindler — sounded the first alarm at the International Agricultural and Forestry Congress in Vienna in 1890. They spoke out at that gathering about the usefulness of local cultivars ('landraces') and warned of the danger that losing them would pose to future crop improvements. Von Proskowetz had already carried out extensive collecting of barley landraces in Moravia. He was moved not only by his conviction of their importance for breeding new varieties, but also by his concern that if no action were taken they could disappear forever[8]. Von Proskowetz was certainly something of a prophet.

Then came Vavilov. Nikolai Ivanovich Vavilov was a Russian scientist who in the 1920s publicly brought forward the idea that crops not only had a centre of origin in specific regions of the world where agriculture commenced, but also had centres of diversity. Vavilov reasoned that these centres of diversity were linked to the areas where the crops originated. We now know that this link is not always exact. Ethiopia, one of the centres recognised by Vavilov, harbours the greatest wealth of different barley and emmer wheat varieties[9], but these crops were probably not domesticated there, as wild forms have never been found.

What Vavilov did had never been done before: he documented the world's incredible wealth of plant genetic diversity. Many people, from Portuguese navigators to Dutch colonialists, had taken a great interest in new and exotic species, but Vavilov, even more than von Proskowetz, had a nose for genetic variation within species. He and his colleagues travelled around the world through more than 40 countries, bringing back to the Soviet Union some of the world's largest collections of crop diversity.

As a result of his travels and studies, Vavilov postulated that the world had eight centres of genetic diversity *(see map)*. These were areas where variation within a given crop was strongest. Since Vavilov's time, his map and theories have been worked and reworked by several other people. New centres have been added and new concepts put forward. In any event, Vavilov's point – that there are specific areas of the world that harbour intense crop diversity – still holds valid. Most of the 'Vavilov centres' are associated with the earliest forms of agriculture and very diverse climates and civilisations. And virtually all of them are in what today is called the Third World.

Maize, the potato, pumpkin and tomato all originate from Latin America. Soybean, oranges and apricots come from China. Foods as familiar to us as lentils, rice, chickpeas, aubergine or cucumber were all domesticated in Asia. For diversity in sorghum, millet, coffee, cotton and a wide range of other crops, you go to Africa. As 'gene centres' for these crops, developing countries are our major source of breeding materials to adapt these plants to new pests and diseases, climate change and new production systems.

Despite our relative genetic poverty, Europe does harbour two centres of diversity for cultivated crops: the Mediterranean and the European-Siberian regions. Not too many species actually originated in these zones, but they have been an important area of 'secondary' genetic diversification due to the many kinds of cultures and peoples tending these crops in various environments.

The Mediterranean centre of diversity includes all of Southern Europe and also takes in the coastal areas of the Near East and North Africa. Turkey, a major centre of diversity in and of itself, is considered part of the Near Eastern region. Southern Europe can boast several truly indigenous crops such as the olive, grape, cabbage, beet, radish and lupin bean. The first two may seem obvious. Who, after all, could possibly imagine a Spanish or Italian meal without olive oil or wine? The cabbage family also has quite a history in Europe – and a very complex taxonomy. Wild kale probably arose on the Mediterranean shorelines in ancient times. People selected various forms for their leaves, buds, shoots and inflorescences giving rise to such different forms as the heading cabbage (red, white and Savoy), cauliflower, broccoli and swedes. Many of these were Italian creations. Savoy or Milan cabbages came from there while broccoli was developed in Italy as late as the 17th century. Then, of

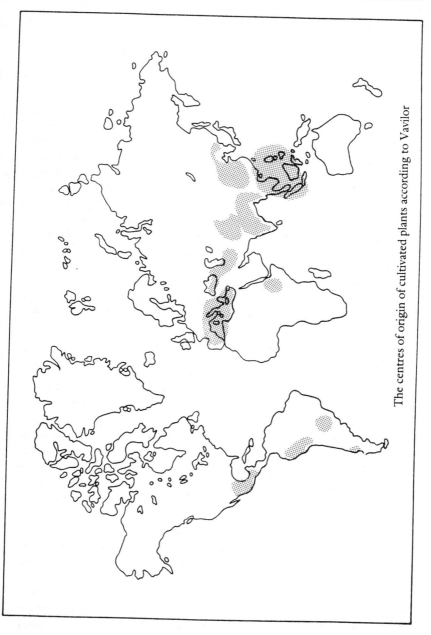

The centres of origin of cultivated plants according to Vavilor

course, there is calabrese (or asparagus broccoli) from Calabria. A most recent innovation in the cabbage family was the development of the Brussels sprout, obviously in Belgium, less than 200 years ago.

The beet family is also connected to Europe. Wild sea beets on the Mediterranean and Atlantic coasts were domesticated very long ago and then split into two directions. Some were selected by people for their tangy green leaves, basically as a cooking vegetable, giving rise to the chards or spinach beets that Aristotle wrote of and are still cherished today. Others were later selected for their sweet root, to become the common garden beet. Fodder beet is said to have been developed in the Netherlands. As for the sugar beet some say it derives from varieties developed in Poland while others credit the Germans for having bred it. Today, this young crop has almost outstripped traditional sugar cane and accounts for over half of the world's sugar production.

But cabbages and beets are just a part of Europe's heritage. The Mediterranean has been home to a whole range of herbs, condiments, medicinal plants and trees. Savory, sage, rosemary, lavender, thyme, laurel, coriander, parsley, the caper bush, the saffron crocus, the cork oak, carob, and the stone pine (providing pine nuts) are just some.

The other European centre of diversity is the Euro-Siberian one. Eastern Europe is home of the hop and certain root crops like horseradish, turnips and parsnip. Many forages and grasses, such as alfalfa, fescue, brome, clover and trefoil, diversified into a rather large spread of varieties in this region. Other crops, such as flax, carrots, sunflower, walnut and lettuce, also have broad genetic ranges in the area.

Siberia is home to a range of fruit-bearing trees that have adapted to the extreme cold typical of Central European winters. One example is the Mongolian or Steppe cherry. It is concentrated beyond the Volga and throughout southern Siberia, where it withstands temperatures below –50° Celsius![10] The apple also derives from this area, particularly the European zones of the former USSR. From West to East, Europe is also an important centre of diversity for spelt wheat[11], peppers, currants, berries and a range of stone fruits[12].

While the development of these relatively indigenous crops have been important to the history of our economies in Europe, a large share of our heritage was initially imported from the Third World: the tomato, potato, rice, peppers, beans, squash and so on. Over the centuries, these tropical crops were acclimatised, adapted and adopted into local farming systems throughout Europe. And in that process, farmers and gardeners created a wealth of different varieties appropriate for their own local needs and realities.

## The heritage makers

People were breeding plants long before the science of genetics was given a name. Partly this was out of necessity. You can't just up and move from southern Greece to Denmark and expect your barley to perform the same way. As people travelled, as civilisations came and went, so too did a plethora of crop varieties come into existence fashioned by the hands of farming and gardening families throughout Europe. The diversity of our climates and soils, and the evolution of pests and disease, meant that permanently adapting crops was a matter of survival.

A critical factor that made all this possible was the genetic variation generously offered by nature and astutely manipulated by people throughout time. Before plant breeding became a science and an industry, it was an art. Seeds were continuously selected and saved. Every house had its seed store and every village 'its' particular bean or barley. And year after year, generation after generation, the seeds were handed down as part of the family treasure. They were also given as wedding gifts, exchanged for different varieties across village boundaries, and placed in tombs when an elder died.

When maize was brought from the New World after Columbus, farmers in Portugal and Italy took to the new crop and created a wide range of local 'populations' as they adapted them to their climates and cultures. These landraces were highly diverse but stable crop types, and were the backbone of farming until professional breeders started producing pure and stable forms. Today, they are more popularly known as 'folk varieties', since people fashioned them. For Portuguese farmers, the value of developing and cultivating local landraces surely lay in profitting from the very high adaptation of maize to their environment. These folk varieties are extremely well-suited to the particular soils and specific micro-climates that abound in the Mediterranean, and which farmers generally controlled very well. A hillside exposed to northern winds or a river valley offering a peculiar combination of humidity and soil nutrients will support different varieties. And as these local landraces co-evolve with pests and diseases, they often provide a fair level of yield security.

Ryes, barleys, oats and wheats were often diversified at the local level to fit technological change on the farm. Experiments in new cropping patterns to combat troublesome diseases or adapt cereals to harsh soils when forests were cleared or wetlands drained resulted in a range of local farmer varieties adapted to specific regions. A widespread practice in traditional cereal production was actually mixing different species on the same plot. For example, English farmers in the Middle Ages commonly grew barley with oats, wheat with rye, or a cereal mixed with a legume. Different regions of the country were characterised by their peculiar mixture. Farmers in East Anglia were known to cultivate oats with peas or vetches, while others specialised in wheat, barley and rye. According to Jules Pretty, the mixtures were probably meant to result in 'smother crops', whereby competition between the crops helped to minimise the growth of weeds and thus make harvests more secure. As records show that there was not necessarily a productive advantage to growing these mixtures in terms of higher yield, farmers obviously valued security and sustainability by averting crop failure over the quest for superior output[13].

During the Renaissance in France, farmers also often grew rye and winter wheat together. Their logic was that since rye grew taller, it would protect the wheat from frost damage. Later, a system of sowing oats and barley into sprouting wheat fields to manage soils and secure a stable harvest became popular[14].

In the Alps, farmers traditionally developed and grew a range of different potatoes in the same plot. This avoided or at least limited the degeneration of the tubers' performance. Farmers knew that if you grew each variety separately to make it easier to sort them later, in a couple of years the lonely varieties started to lose certain features that made a decent yield possible. Growing them in mixtures provided protection against these breakdowns. In Oisans, a pre-Alpine region of France, farmers used to say that mixing potatoes in the field made them 'jealous' of each other and provided some competition for growth[15]. Modern scientists now explain this otherwise: mixing and rotating your potato varieties makes agronomic sense, as it fends off the accumulation of viruses that build up in plots sown to one variety alone and are inevitably transmitted to the next generation.

Throughout the ages, farmers have not only continuously innovated and experimented in farming practices, thus generating broader genetic diversity, but also diffused the results. Informal farmer-to-farmer exchange mechanisms allowed innovations – including new crops, varieties, production systems and technologies – to spread and be tested by others for adaptation and adoption. Seed exchange was particularly important for the development and maintenance of genetic diversity on the farm. In 18th century England, farmers swapped seeds not only to have access to new varieties to test them out, but also to avoid merchants who were suspected of mixing seed stocks and offering a dubious product[16].

While survival, through yield security and soil and water management, was surely the driving force behind the development of most folk varieties, many odd factors contribute to the creation of this diversity. For instance, the end product has to meet consumer demands. Wheat and barley were taken through many stages of diversification in Europe as they were grown in some cultures to make beer or syrup, in others to make gruel, and in yet others later on to grind into flour and produce bread or pasta. The same can be said about potatoes, a crop introduced in the 16th century from Latin America. As it slowly gained popularity on farms and in gardens, some people selected potatoes for boiling and others for frying, creating some varieties with more starch, thinner skins and other characteristics. Peoples' preferences for different foods meant perpetually designing, testing and developing crops to suit those tastes.

Consumer demand is not just utilitarian though, limited to energy costs or cooking customs. It is eminently cultural. As the bourgeoisie rose in Belgium after the 17th century, they took on what might seem a pathological liking for pears because they were considered an 'elegant' fruit. Their mania resulted in the creation of over one thousand distinct pear cultivars being grown in the stately gardens of this tiny country by the end of the last century[17]. Just to impress!

Sometimes even religious affiliations governed the variety of potato you grew. Philippe Marchenay, a French ethnobotanist, found that in Saint-Vérain, the highest village of Europe (2,000 metres), it was customary for the Protestants to grow red potatoes, while the yellow ones were the domain of Catholics![18] Why exactly, no one could say. This may seem a far-out example, but our food plants can and often do have strong links to our collective identities. Even today, urban gardeners often plant their own village variety of tomato to keep those links with their roots and culture intact.

Yet, cultivated plants are not the only element of our crop heritage in Europe. People have always tended and picked wild, spontaneous or semi-domesticated plants. François Couplan's monumental work documenting the role of wild plants in our food system shows that edible semi-domesticates have played a major role in feeding people and animals throughout European history.[19] In Britain, for example, economic management of wild plants was extremely important to rural families in the Middle Ages. As half of the peasant population had holdings that were too small to assure subsistence, they had to supplement both diets and income from external sources in order to survive. Wild plants were considered a critical resource in this respect and access to woodlands and other sources were carefully and equitably managed by local communities[20]. Even today, carefully monitoring and gathering undomesticated plants – be they mushrooms, medicinal plants, forages, seaweed, nuts, asparagus, salad greens, forest berries or wild fruits – is still an active part of our culture, leisure and perhaps even sustenance in many parts of Europe.

Millions of anonymous rural folk – down to our parents and grandparents – throughout Europe have spent some part of their lives keeping this heritage alive, but the act of saving a seed has become threatened with extinction by the drive toward industrialisation and integrated market economies. Today we are told that seed saving is better done by others: governments are now storing the old seeds for posterity and industry is producing newer and better seeds all the time.

The decline in ordinary people's role in managing the wealth created, managed and handed down to us from our ancestors and relatives is a very dangerous trend. Our heritage of different crop varieties adapted to different cultures and agricultures can really thrive only where it was generated: in our backyards and farms, guided by our knowledge and needs. When you take seeds away from local farmers and gardeners and their production systems, you are severing something very deep: the intimate relations of people with the history embodied in plants and their right to stewardship over a collective patrimony, their family's, their village's, their region's.

Culturally, this is very disturbing. We see it in Europe, the United States and throughout the Third World today, as agricultures 'develop' and become more industrialised. Shifting control and management of people's crop heritage from gardeners and farmers over to State institutes and boards of corporations promotes social and ethnic alienation. But technically and politically as well, it is a trend that must be reversed. When the development, conservation and production of planting materials is taken away from farmers and monopolised by government or industry, people are losing vital control over a very important resource to shape their lives. As put so well by Cary Fowler and Pat Mooney of RAFI, *'Someone else's seeds imply someone else's needs.'*[21] Invariably so. Our crop heritage was born of the people and should remain under their control to continue fashioning change and evolution. When this link is severed, it will take a hell of a lot of work to refashion it.

# 2: Diversity's decline

Less than twenty years ago you could drive through the villages of Germany or France around September–October and still find a plethora of regionally-adapted apples: some were good for baking in pies, others for making cider or sauce, yet others for eating right off the tree. But consumption alone did not make the variety. Certain types favoured high altitudes, others were less resistant to the cold. Some kept exceptionally well in the attic or cellar, while others had fruit that matured unevenly over several months.

Today, however, most supermarkets and food shops in Western Europe offer essentially three types of apples: a red one (the Starking, from the USA), a yellow one (the so-called Golden 'Delicious', also from the USA) and a green one (the Granny Smith, or pippin, from Australia). When packaged together, they look like a traffic light signalling to the consumer: this much variety, no more.

A couple of years ago, a survey done in the southeast of France showed that until this century, the Provençal diet was rich with 250 plant species, including vegetables, fruits and condiments. Today, barely 60 are cultivated in the region, of which only 30 make up the bulk of local consumption[1]. The number of species available or in use is one measure of the genetic diversity of our food system, the number of varieties within the same crop is another. Greece, which once harboured a considerable array of local landraces of wheat developed in the different climatic zones of the country, has lost all but 5 per cent of this heritage[2]. Over the past few decades alone, Greek farmers have been encouraged to abandon their regionally-adapted types and grow a few ultra-modern varieties developed in Mexico. Most of what the farmers discarded through this process is gone forever.

Four mutually reinforcing factors are pushing Europe's food and farming systems towards greater uniformity: adverse agricultural policies, the concentration of the seed sector, plant breeding research geared towards increased homogeneity and the laws governing the seed supply.

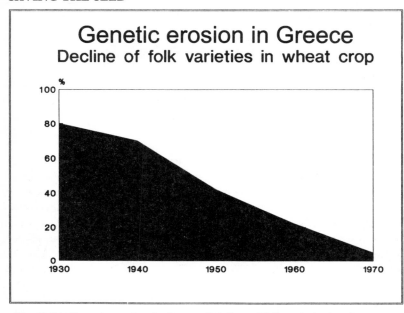

**Graph 1**:  Genetic erosion in Greece: Decline of folk varieties in wheat crop

Together, these four potent factors are part and parcel of what we generally refer to as the industrialisation of agriculture.

Since the end of the Second World War, and the implementation of the Marshall Plan, farming in Western Europe has undergone the most profound transformation since people started domesticating plants. Keen on creating a cheaply-fed urban labour force for rising industries and achieving food security at lower consumer prices, governments and industry went to work 'rationalising' and modernising the agricultural sector. Most of this took place through the widespread introduction of farm machinery, the development of chemical fertilisers and pesticides, and genetic manipulation of crops and animals to integrate them into the new production systems and ensure higher yields. At the same time, cheap credit was offered to farmers to restructure farmlands and intensify production units.

Much has been said about these changes. On one side, we are told that Europe now feeds itself and has become an important agricultural trade partner on the world market. Politicians incessantly argue that consumers want cheaper and cheaper food and they are getting it. But this is only true in comparison to prices for industrial commodities. Food prices at the market are in fact rising: it is the percentage of their total income that people spend on food that is dropping. On the other side, people are increasingly concerned about the abuse of chemicals on the farm and the residues that contaminate their food and water supply. Others point to the disastrous impact of the European Community's (EC) price policies for developing countries and the dumping of its products on the world market. And virtually everybody has started to worry about the cost. According to a recent report on industrial farming in *The Ecologist*, agricultural subsidies, representing at least 60 per cent of the Community's entire budget, cost EC taxpayers $40 billion a year, two-thirds of which is spent on 'managing' surpluses and subsidising exports.[3]

While we all see surpluses and subsidies at the centre of global trade wars today, we shouldn't overlook the fact that farm prices have been steadily reduced and production progressively concentrated among the few who can make it. From 1963 to 1983, cereal prices in the EC were cut by 45 per cent. From 1983 to 1990, they dropped another 30 per cent. Consumers might have expected that this devaluation of food, compared to other commodities, would result in cheaper prices. In fact, food prices are increasing. And much of that price increase goes to the input and processing industries, the trading companies and the shops. Each time we buy a loaf of bread in Europe, only 15 per cent of its price represents the cost of the wheat grown by a farmer. The rest goes to milling, baking, packaging, transport and marketing.

This incredible price gap between farm and supermarket prices reflects the growing distance between producers and consumers, and gives an ever growing share of the value of food to industry. Almost 90 per cent of the food we consume is processed. The power of the food industry is overwhelming. As the physical and psychological distance grows between farmers and consumers, between the land and the cities, the food industry gains more manouvering space and earns bigger profits from the gap between the two. Yet, the real burden of lower prices has landed on the farmers and pushed them into the spiral of raising productivity to make up for the losses. The drive for cheaper and cheaper food has brought with it incredibly high social and environmental costs that we have yet to calculate.

What we can calculate is the concentration and intensification of the system. Today, 75 per cent of the EC's milk is produced by a quarter of our dairy farms and 60 per cent of the cereals come from 6 per cent of the grain farms. A full 80 per cent of the pork output comes from 10 per cent of the pig producers. As for poultry, 90 per cent comes from 10 per cent of the poultry farms. At the bottom line, we are left with about ten million farmers today, with nearly half a million closing down or going out of business each year. Young farmers are completely discouraged to continue farming, even if their economic situation might allow them to go on. The EC encourages this social erosion in the name of efficiency and offers early retirement measures to close down small farms where there are no sons or daughters willing to maintain them. In order to create larger holdings and highly intensive production schemes, the EC might close down more than half of the farms within the next five years. More than 50 per cent of EC farmers are over 55 years old and might be enticed to take the early retirement offer.

The result of all this has been not just an ecological, but also a socio-economic mess. Farmers are essentially told what to grow, how to grow it and what price they will be paid for it. Consumers are told that they are paying less for food at the supermarket but are never shown the bill for the astronomic production and export subsidies dished out to farmers to make up the difference between world and European market prices. For everyone, the loss of choice and of the freedom to choose has been spectacular. The mirage of products and packages in the supermarket simply conceals the enormous concentration of the food supply.

We are fast losing control of agriculture in Europe – that is, whatever link farming bears to culture at all. Modernisation and development are perfectly noble ideas, but when they are reduced to one model or strategy for production imposed on everybody from a small group of policymakers they can become eminently destructive forces. As regionally adapted farming systems and the farmers who fashioned them give way to a handful of high output factory farms, we are sacrificing long term alternatives to the immediate push for productivity. All the talk today about 'sustainability' has come about *because* short-term interests have taken over long term strategic thinking in almost every sphere of our economy.

The tremendous pressure towards ever greater homogeneity in Europe – from the food we eat to the clothes we wear – is undermining the basis of what is left of genetic and cultural diversity. In the plant breeding sector, the myriad family seed companies that once populated our regions have almost all been bought out by a handful of chemical and pharmaceutical multinationals. Industrial agriculture needs and breeds uniformity: ecosystems stripped to their barest minimum, a farming population made up of a few specialised entrepreneurs, a consumer model easy to serve. Yet uniformity, be it in nature or society, is highly unstable and sensitive to new and potentially explosive pressures. The standardisation and concentration of the food chain and of our increasingly market-driven cultures has put the alternatives at risk. When we want or need them anew, they may no longer be available. The question society has to ask itself is whether the costs are truly worth the benefits.

## Breeding uniformity

Farmers have been breeders ever since agriculture began. But breeders have been scientists only for the past two hundred years or so – a minute fraction of plant breeding's history. The whys and hows of genetic recombinations that underpin crop improvement started to be deciphered in the 18th century, in countries such as France, Germany, Sweden and England. Rich landowners, imitating the royal elite, set up special gardens where they introduced and experimented with exotic species, with a heavy emphasis on ornamentals. Other families set up special breeding operations to develop new agricultural and horticultural crops for local farming systems.

The Vilmorin-Andrieux family in France were pioneers in Europe's burgeoning plant breeding industry. In the 1770s, they opened the first Vilmorin seed house, outside Paris, where they experimented with and sold a range of both exotic and indigenous species to French farmers: forage beets, swedes, trees and ornamentals from the American colonies. In the 1850s, Louis de Vilmorin through his work on sugar beets figured out a scheme for crossing plants. His method was later applied to wheat and other cereals and became the basis of 'pedigree' breeding, mastered in many European countries for many crops by the late 1800s. Formerly, farmers carried out mass selection of choice individuals, taking what they liked best and reproducing from there. Pedigree breeding, by contrast, arranges a marriage of two plants in order to create new kinds of offspring.

Henry de Vilmorin made pedigree wheat breeding the family's vocation by the 1870s. His first successes were crosses of hardy English squarehead wheats and early-maturing varieties from Aquitaine, resulting in Dattel in 1883. Vilmorin's efforts were a huge success, from Bon Fermier (Good Farmer), released in 1905, through to the famous Vilmorin 27 of 1927, and most French wheats today are direct descendants of these original crosses.

Other European breeders active in the search for new varieties included Rimpau in Germany, who was crossing American and German wheats in the 1880s, and Broekema in the Netherlands. The famous Svalöf breeding station was established in Sweden in 1886, where Nilsson-Ehle was working to understand the logic of these genetic manoeuvres and relationships. Towards the very end of the century Polish and Russian breeders were also active in the field.

Despite this flurry of crossing and observing, it wasn't until the early 20th century that the science of genetics, based on the neglected work of the Austrian monk Gregor Mendel, was given a name and the laws of genetic variation better understood. From the 1920s onwards, plant breeding became a much more widespread activity and networks of farming families increasingly became specialised in selecting, multiplying and selling seed to other farmers. This was the birth of the seed industry as an activity divorced from crop production itself. Certain zones of Europe became specialised in seed production owing to their favourable climates: Bavaria for barley, Pévèle in the north of France for sugar beet and grains, and Brabant in Belgium for several crops[4]. The innovations brought forward by small family enterprises – the Cuthberts in England, Probstdorfer Saatzucht in Austria, Benoist, Desprez and Lepeuple in France, Strube and von Lochow in Germany – were the backbone of modern plant breeding.

The emergence of this private, family-based professional seed sector was greatly facilitated by public research institutes and universities. Scientists collected and stored farmers' landraces to develop new breeding populations. Over the decades, they complemented the private sector by working on crops that were less profitable or more difficult to work with genetically, particularly fruit species. They also helped develop more sophisticated breeding methods. Some companies were able to make a fortune off the backs of this vigorous public sector activity. For example, the French cooperative Limagrain – the world's fourth biggest seed company today – built its whole empire around a variety called LG11, an inbred maize line publicly released by France's National Institute for Agronomic Research after the war. One of Limagrain's technicians found out that simply by increasing the sowing dose of this seed, yields could increase dramatically[5].

The turning point came in the 1960s with the increasing use of chemical- and petrol-based products in agriculture (machine fuel, synthetic fertiliser, herbicides, pesticides and other biocides). Agribusiness started booming on a global scale. And it was not long before the chemical, food processing and pharmaceutical giants took an interest in the seed as a logical area to invest in. The grain traders and food processors, such as Cargill or Continental Grain, could get a better grip over the food chain, from seed to harvest. The chemical and pharmaceutical houses could strike a better marriage between their main product lines and specifically bred varieties. It is simply cheaper, quicker and easier to adapt a plant to chemicals than chemicals to a plant. And as if the logic of commercial control through this kind of synergy in research emphases or in distribution were not compelling enough, new laws that offered monopoly rights over seeds boosted corporate interest in plant breeding significantly.

In the space of just two decades, from 1970 onward, an enormous wave of industrial concentration and corporate investment transformed the face – and orientation – of plant breeding in Europe and in the rest of the industrialised world. Worldwide, more than 500 family businesses have been bought out completely and another 300 have been the subject of financial investments[6]. The old-time names such as Clause, Hilleshög or Van der Haave are still printed on the seed packets, but their owners and capital investors are now Rhône-Poulenc, Sandoz and Suiker Unie, respectively. Today, the global seed market – which represents sales of $15–17 billion a year, of which $5–6 billion are in Europe – is largely controlled by no more than 10 to 20 firms. The top 10 companies control one-fifth of the market and the top 15 nearly a quarter (*see Table 2.1*). This might seem little, if compared, for example, to the concentration in the pesticides industry, where the top 12 companies control 80 per cent of the sales. However, taking into consideration the short time frame in which the takeovers took place, and the intrinsic limitation on widespread market control of a biological, site-specific input, the concentration of the seeds industry is tremendous.

The rising control of the corporate sector over an economic field so vital to our survival, food production, is in and of itself a matter of serious concern. But what has heightened this concern is the fact that the rise of the large private sector in commanding research and development for the future of agriculture is accompanied by a precipitous decline in the public sector's role in this field. Since the 1970s, many West European governments have been slowly pulling out of critical areas of social development such as education, health care and scientific research, leaving it to the private sector to take up the responsibility.

When the British government sold off the prestigious Plant Breeding Institute of Cambridge in 1987, it acted more like a stockbroker than a responsible civil service. The lengthy quest for the highest bid, which the government apparently fed like a fire, led to Unilever's aquisition of the institute. What to do with the genetic resources held in the public domain by PBI appeared to be a secondary consideration. Probably in fear of public dissent, which was already rumbling abroad, the

**Table 2.1:** The world's top seed companies (1991 seed sales in US$ millions)

| Group | Nationality | Main activity | Seed sales |
|---|---|---|---|
| Pioneer | USA | Seeds | 1124 |
| Sandoz[1] | Switzerland | Pharmaceuticals | 660 |
| Limagrain[2] | France | Seeds | 410 |
| Upjohn | USA | Chemicals | 310 |
| ICI | UK | Chemicals | 235 |
| Cargill | USA | Trade | 230 |
| Cebeco | Netherlands | Food processing | 195 |
| Dekalb Genetics | USA | Seeds | 190 |
| Van der Haave | Netherlands | Seeds | 180 |
| Takii | Japan | Chemicals | 170 |
| Aritrois[3] | France | Chemicals | 155 |
| Orsan[4] | France | Chemicals | 152 |
| KWS | Germany | Seeds | 151 |
| Sakata | Japan | Seeds | 150 |
| Ciba-Geigy | Switzerland | Pharmaceuticals | 142 |
| Sanofi[5] | France | Pharmaceuticals | 141 |
| Lubrizol | USA | Chemicals | 115 |
| Provendor[6] | Sweden | Food processing | 110 |
| Royal Sluis | Netherlands | Seeds | 103 |

**Notes:**
(1) Includes Hilleshög, bought from Provendor in 1989
(2) Includes Nickerson, bought from Shell in 1990
(3) Subsidiary of Rhône-Poulenc and Orsan; includes Clause, bought in 1989
(4) Subsidiary of Lafarge-Coppée
(5) Subsidiary of Elf Aquitaine
(6) Subsidiary of Volvo

*Source:* Pierre-Benoît Joly, INRA, personal communication, August 1992.

government and Unilever agreed to entrust the collection to the John Innes Institute. The same thing nearly happened itself a few years later in France, when the National Institute for Agronomic Research (INRA) was rumoured to have conducted two years of quiet negotiations with the French chemical giant Rhône-Poulenc to sell off all or a number of its public plant breeding stations. At the last moment, INRA apparently got cold feet and backed out.

In the field of agricultural research, the role of the public sector is critical – one we cannot forfeit in the name of limited, short-term interests. By its very nature, the private sector will only invest where there is a quick buck to be made. In plant breeding, this is largely limited to applied research on annual crops that can be hybridised at a reasonable cost and marketed over the largest area. Who is supposed to do the basic research and development, assuming that is necessary? Who will invest in the crops that industry cannot make a profit on? Who will serve the market niches – including marginal areas and farmers that cannot afford expensive technology – that are invisible to and bypassed by the global seedsmen? A public–private balance is essential to provide options and alternatives. Pressure to let vested interests breed our crops and withdraw public funding for research is destroying that balance and compromising our range of options heavily.

## Uniformity from the lab

In assessing the state of the genetic base of European farming, a first and simple factor to look at is the amount of varieties actually offered by the breeders. We are often told that the private sector, with its incentives to invest, provides more varieties for the seed market, and thus does a better service to diversity. A look at the brief history of industrial plant breeding shows that this is certainly not always the case. Take France, for example. The pioneering seed company Vilmorin-Andrieux offered, on its own, in 1925, almost as many varieties of some vegetables as the *entire French national list* in 1981! For specific vegetables, such as certain beans, cabbages, garden beet, melon and onion, this single family company had more varieties to offer than are now available on the entire French seed market (*Table 2.2*).

While numbers can be stunning, a more complex and significant factor to consider is how genetically diverse the different varieties really are. It might be nice to have hundreds of different wheat varieties on the market, but how distinct are they from each other, genetically speaking? Do they have different forms of resistance to rusts or mildew, or identical ones? Are they built on the same yield complexes or distinct ones? What

Table 2.2: The vegetable supply in France

| Species | Number of varieties | | |
|---|---|---|---|
| | *Vilmorin-Andrieux 1981* | *National Catalogue 1925* | *Change over 55 years* |
| Aubergine | 16 | 21 | + 31% |
| Bush beans | | | |
| - pod beans | 79 | 52 | − 34% |
| - string beans | 42 | 190 | + 352% |
| Cabbage: white/red | 59 | 44 | − 25% |
| Carrot | 27 | 51 | + 89% |
| Garden beet | 21 | 12 | − 43% |
| Leek | 15 | 31 | + 106% |
| Melon | 59 | 44 | − 25% |
| Onion | 73 | 35 | − 52% |
| Runner beans | | | |
| - pod beans | 29 | 9 | − 69% |
| - string beans | 42 | 22 | − 48% |
| TOTAL | 462 | 511 | + 11% |

*Source:* Bertrand Schweisguth, 'Le maintien et la valorisation de la diversité des plantes légumières: role de la recherche agronomique' in *La diversité des plantes légumières: hier, aujourd'hui et demain*, JATBA, Paris, 1986, p. 195.

proportion of hybrid maizes or sunflowers are derived from a common inbred parental line? Only at this level can we assess true genetic diversity among cultivars. Again the picture for European agriculture is hardly encouraging.

Generally speaking, the history of plant breeding, with its progressive concentration of actors and recycling of well-performing germ plasm, is leading agriculture into a genetic downward spiral. Some call it 'the funnel effect', as illustrated by graph 2. Starting with a relatively wide selection of landraces, or folk varieties, collected from farmers and gardeners throughout Europe, institutional breeding has been an exercise in perfecting and reperfecting that material, to such an extent that almost all of the top breeders are basically using only highly purified and stable 'elite' material – which is extremely uniform. While major corporations usually do not reveal exactly what germplasm they are using, this overall impression was recently confirmed in private by a representative of Ciba-Geigy[7]

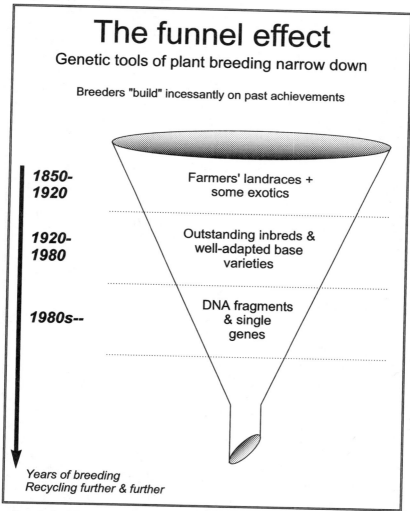

# The funnel effect
## Genetic tools of plant breeding narrow down

Breeders "build" incessantly on past achievements

**1850-1920**   Farmers' landraces + some exotics

**1920-1980**   Outstanding inbreds & well-adapted base varieties

**1980s--**   DNA fragments & single genes

Years of breeding
Recycling further & further

**Graph 2:** The funnel effect: Genetic tools of plant breeding narrow down

In 1986, a survey was carried out among European breeders working with the onion family (*Alliaceae*, which includes onions, leeks, garlic and shallots) and with barley, to determine what kind of genetic materials they use and how useful genebank collections of varieties are to them. The results of the study are alarming. They show that for both crop groups and for the main objectives, breeders predominantly use elite materials composed of breeders' lines and advanced cultivars from breeders' collections (*Tables 2.3 and 2.4*). Breeders are often reluctant to use wild species and landraces, as it is difficult to transfer the right gene from a wild source into a well-adapted cultivar without transferring a lot of genetic garbage along with it. They are much happier to work with an already proven and predictable breeding base, which means they are recycling uniformity. This is exactly the kind of breeding approach that reinforces the funnel effect.

**Table 2.3:** Sources of germplasm used by breeders in Europe (% of total)

|  | *When breeding for* | | |
| --- | --- | --- | --- |
|  | *Disease resistance* | *Stress tolerance* | *Yield increase* |
| *Barley breeders use:* | | | |
| Breeders' materials | 59% | 71% | 85% |
| Genebank materials | 41% | 28% | 15% |
| *Allium breeders use:* | | | |
| Breeders' materials | 80% | 91% | 84% |
| Genebank materials | 20% | 9% | 16% |

*Source:* Adapted by GRAIN from UNDP/IBPGR, *Report of a Barley Workshop*, IBPGR, Rome, 1986.

When we look at wheat, the narrowness of the genetic base is also shocking. Annick Le Blanc and her colleagues Jean Koenig and Louis Jestin at the INRA station in Clermont-Ferrand, have been studying the pedigree of French wheats and barley down to the molecular level. Their findings confirm the general impression: *'Genetic variability of French wheat cultivars has decreased, the breeders having crossed only a few well-known progenitors.'* [8] Researchers have shown that all of France's current wheats are descendants of one folk variety called Noé (or Noah),

**Table 2.4:** Type of germplasm used by breeders in Europe (% of total)

|  | When breeding for | | |
|---|---|---|---|
|  | Disease resistance | Stress tolerance | Yield increase |
| **Barley breeders use:** | | | |
| Elite materials* | 68% | 63% | 96% |
| Landraces | 22% | 28% | 4% |
| Weedy relatives | 4% | 3% | — |
| Wild materials | 6% | 6% | — |
| **Allium breeders use:** | | | |
| Elite materials* | 46% | 59% | 82% |
| Landraces | 31% | 28% | 9% |
| Weedy relatives | 5% | 6% | 6% |
| Wild materials | 18% | 6% | 3% |

* Advanced cultivars and breeders' lines

*Source:* Adapted by GRAIN from UNDP/IBPGR, *Report of a Barley Workshop,* IBPGR, Rome, 1986.

a population developed by the villagers of Odessa, in the Ukraine, last century. However, some modern breeders still contest these findings. Michel Desprez, of the Desprez family which in the 1940s developed Cappelle, a variety that can be traced in most of today's French wheats, is hard to convince. '*I don't believe that the variability of cultivars has been reduced,*' he told GRAIN. '*On the contrary, for many plants, such as wheat or barley, the genetic basis of the varieties marketed now is much wider than the same basis thirty years ago.*'[9] But he offered no evidence to support his belief.

In Germany, most wheat varieties carry Carsten VIII in their pedigree. Of the seven winter wheat cultivars released in Germany in 1986, five derive from Caribo, which is itself a cross between France's Capelle and Carsten[10]. In all these cases we can see clearly that breeders started off with a minimal range of well-adapted landraces, stabilised some 'top performance' breeding lines geared for high yield, and have been recycling this narrow pool since. The motto has clearly been, *'Cross the best and hope for the best*[11]*.'*

When we look at the sugar beet varieties being churned out in Germany and the Netherlands today, the narrowness of the germplasm base has breeders openly alarmed. According to Anton Zeven, of the Agricultural University at Wageningen, *'European sugar beet cultivars all carry the same genotype for beet yellow virus susceptibility,'* a major threat to beet production[12]. Researchers in Germany also point out that today's sugar beet hybrids also carry the same identical source of cytoplasmic male sterility (CMS)[13]. This is no minor problem: a fungus caused a 15 per cent harvest loss of American maize in 1971, due to widespread use of one source of CMS there.

As to the cabbage family, breeders only maintain and use highly uniform inbred lines, despite the wealth of landraces developed by European farmers and gardeners over the centuries. Breeders themselves fear that large scale hybridisation of cabbage-related crops could replace these landraces if they are not collected and ultimately wipe-out a treasure chest of resources for future breeding[14].

The point is not only that most of our crop varieties are remixtures of each other, offering little real diversity to farmers, but also that diversity has disappeared. As Anton Zeven of the Agricultural University at Wageningen puts it, *'Is the genetic variation of the present day cultivars in the Netherlands less than that of all the landraces grown here before? Nobody knows.'*[15] And we may never know, for many of those landraces are gone for ever. Many people think it is likely that there was greater genetic variability among our complex old folk varieties and locally adapted landraces than among our current hybrids and highly elite seeds, which are so genetically close to each other except for a chromosome here or an enzyme there. Yet to others, that single chromosome or minute enzyme makes all the difference in the world between one tomato and another. Is this diversity?

Breeding uniformity is not only a question of what materials you use and re-use, but what you breed for. Over the past decades, in many cases the single major focus has been yield, to the detriment of disease resistance, taste, nutrition, and other qualitative factors. In French wheat, again, the story is clear. From Table 2.5 we can see that over time, wheat breeders have focused their attention on early ripening and yield, rather than disease resistance or bread-making quality. Aside from the glaring fixation on yield, the assumption was obviously that susceptibility to disease can be compensated through chemical treatments, which indeed have become necessary with this type of breeding. The lack of focus on baking qualities, results in the current situation where France – a major bread-eating country – is obliged to import decent wheat from Germany to meet the requirements of the French baking industry[16].

**Table 2.5:** Changing breeding priorities in French wheat

| Variety (date of release) | Rust resistance | Mildew resistance | Baking quality | Yield |
|---|---|---|---|---|
| Vilmorin 27 (1927) | 4 | 4 | 4 | 1 |
| Cappelle (1946) | 2 | 4 | 4 | 3 |
| Etoile de Choisy (1950) | 2 | 4 | 2 | 3 |
| Capitole (1964) | 4 | 5 | 5 | 5 |
| Top (1970) | 5 | 4 | 3 | 5.5 |
| Talent (1973) | 1 | 5.5 | 3.5 | 6.5 |
| Fidel (1978) | 3 | 5 | 4 | 7 |
| Thésée (1983) | 1 | 4 | 4 | 8 |

*Scorecard of 1–10 for*

*Source:* Adapted by GRAIN from Alain Bonjean and Emanuel Picard, *Les céréales à paille*, Softword/Groupe ITM, 1990, p. 87.

There is really very little evidence available to paint a clear picture of how diverse (and secure) or narrow (and insecure) the genetic base of our food supply really is. No serious research has been carried out to assess where crop breeding is going with respect to genetic diversity; in fact throughout GRAIN's survey on the question, many public sector scientists concerned about genetic erosion complained about this. The little information we have often seems anecdotal and there are huge differences of opinion as to what diversity really is and how you measure it. Part of the problem is that the privatisation of plant breeding has brought with it the privatisation of germ plasm collections and information about breeding programmes. Another part of the problem is that no one has taken this question seriously enough to find an answer to it.

The answer is important both for farmers and for consumers, but we can make judgements based only on general impressions. It is clear that what is coming out of today's breeding system is uniformity. Part of this is because breeders are pressured to service an increasingly homogenous and intensified agriculture, focused on gaining yield over any other factor. But another part of this is because the big breeders of today look for quick and cheap solutions to problems in the field or in their market share. This leads to a narrow fascination with single, quick-shot super genes rather than working with broad variation, obsolete or wild materials, and complex genetic structures.

In fact, when sounding out breeders about future developments in this respect, it seems that many place their hopes on genetic engineering and other tools of biotechnology to bring more diversity into the European crop sector. Now that we can cross species barriers by genetic engineering we can create whole new combinations of genetic material. With molecular markers we will be able meticulously to locate specific genes for minute functions in plants and move them around more precisely. And, so we are told, all of this will bring novel genetic variation into our crops.

We have our doubts, and very serious ones indeed. The current narrow focus on single gene remedies to major problems in crop production ignores the fact that plants contain tens of thousands of genes that contribute to the plant's physical make up, which itself interacts in a specific and highly variable environment. Reducing this diversity to its minute, molecular components destroys its very nature. Plants may be composed of sequences of DNA, but focusing on parts shatters our vision of the whole.

Some scientists also have grave doubts about whether a molecular approach to crop breeding will bring diversity to European agriculture. They see the limits and even the dangers of the technology, but they also point to the economic framework within which biotechnology is being developed. Franco Lorenzetti of the Institute for Plant Genetic Improvement in Perugia is concerned about how new ways of producing seeds for farmers could result in a loss of variation on the farm. '*The manipulation of the mode of reproduction and possibility of using tissue culture and artificial seed production for agricultural crops could have great negative impacts on genetic diversity.*'[17] Both of the novel approaches Lorenzetti mentions are aimed at mass producing identical clones, which could easily be wiped out by a disease epidemic if grown on large holdings. A great number of researchers point out that biotechnology can only provide a few new genes that will have to be inserted in current cultivars, resulting in no major introduction of diversity.

While the technology has its limits, the economic environment will have a large role to play in determining the impact of biotechnology on

**48**

crop genetic diversity in Europe. For one thing, lots of people point to the price tag attached to these high-tech approaches. In the view of Hans Doll of the Riso National Laboratory in Roskilde, Denmark, '*As biotechnology is so costly to utilise, it is very likely that only the "big crops", will be improved this way. Therefore it is very likely that biotechnology will result in a reduction in the number of cultivated species.*'[18] Richard Flavell, head of the John Innes Institute in Norwich, a hothouse of plant biotech research in the UK, goes even further. '*I would expect [biotechnology] to reinforce the trends to fewer varieties created by fewer breeders.*'[19] The erosion – corporate and genetic – could be tremendous.

The true genius of plant breeding lies in the development of vast genetic complexes, such as those that constitute the landraces and folk seeds our great grandparents handed down to us. They did not know genetics as such, but they worked with whole plant populations within complex environments. Moving a microscopic fragment of DNA from one plant cell into another will not create genetic – or biological – diversity. Nor will it return to millions of European farmers the stability, security and ecological dynamics that have been removed from their fields.

## Erosion on the farm

In the second half of 1990, GRAIN carried out a survey among public agronomic research institutes, genebanks, conservation organisations and industry in Western Europe. We asked for concrete information on genetic erosion at the national and European levels. Response was quite high, showing a keen (and somewhat morbid) interest in the subject. The general feedback was that no one knows with any great precision what has been lost. No analytical statistics are available on genetic erosion in Europe, just a vast swamp of muddy impressions. As Louis Jestin of INRA's Cereal Genetic Resources Programme put it, '*Reliable data are simply lacking, and imagination should not replace facts.*'[20] We certainly agree. But at the same time, lack of imagination should not replace the need to come to grips with the causes and magnitude of the problem.

There are several ways to assess genetic erosion on the farm in Europe. One is to look at the number of crops or species being grown in a given region or country. Another is to look at the number of varieties per crop being planted to the fields.

# SAVING THE SEED

## Losing crops

Historically, farmers have continuously shifted their cropping patterns in response to changing demands from their families, environments or external markets. In the process, they have imported and adapted new crops and abandoned old ones. However, that process had never been geared towards uniformity to any great fashion until the past century. The most visible form of genetic erosion is the decline in the total number of crops we grow and live from. The range of cereals, vegetables, fruits and medicinal plants – not to mention forest and industrial crops – that form part of an ordinary farming system in Europe today has dropped vastly. As mixed cropping systems succumb to monocultures, and specialisation in only one or two crops takes over, the range of species in our food supply is dwindling more and more.

In wheats, for example, the rustic emmers, spelts and einkorns have all but given way to the uniform soft and durum types (for making bread and pasta, respectively). Scientific expeditions throughout the Mediterranean and Central Europe, carried out jointly by Italy and East Germany since 1980, report the tremendous decline of these hardy cereals among local farmers[21]. They can usually be found only in mountainous regions of Italy or Greece and the eastern zones of Moravia and Slovakia where they are grown in mixtures, that provide for enormous heterogeneity and stability of yield. In Calabria, southern Italy, once a cereal farming zone, rural emigration has been so strong that by 1986 the only relic of wheat cultivation to be found was one solitary farmer who was growing durum and bread wheat together, to improve the quality of the flour[22].

Cultivation of oats and rye are also declining as forage grasses and legumes such as silage maize and colza take their place. Both of these cereals were the backbone of many rural economies in Europe because they were hardy, could withstand difficult environments and provided a range of outputs on the farm. But today, rare are the farms in Europe where you can still find cultivated rye growing with its wild progenitor *Secale strictum* lining the edge or smack in the middle of the field, to promote the natural exchange of genetic characters[23]!

Despite the fact that many of the crops developed in Europe were valued for their health care function from the start, the regression of medicinal and aromatic plants has been marked in most countries over the past decades. Pre-war Germany was the site of 10,000 hectares devoted to the cultivation of medicinal plants. Today, that figure has dropped to 1,100 hectares of which 700 are in Bavaria[24]. The situation may be similar in other European countries and valuable landraces will surely by lost if local gardeners do not pass them on. In fact, according to Vernon Heywood of IUCN, the World Conservation Union, '*IBPGR [the International Board for Plant Genetic Resources] was asked a few years ago to look into the question of genetic erosion in medicinal plants and was unable to discover any. Subsequently they admitted that they had not made a very good job of this study and that there is indeed quite a lot of evidence for such genetic erosion, both in Europe and elsewhere.*'[25]

In Spain and Portugal, as well as other Mediterranean countries, legumes such as vetch peas, cowpeas, lupin beans, favas (or broad beans), lentils and chickpeas have long been major crops alongside cereals, providing a stable diet for people and animals and fertilising the soils with precious nitrogen from the air. As well, a whole range of 'minor legumes' were a traditional part of farming systems until a few years ago. These include chickling vetch, bitter vetch and lentil vetch. Except for the common *Phaseolus* bean, genetic erosion has been great in most of these crops, and many species and varieties have disappeared from the farms[26].

Hard data on what farmers and gardeners are sowing in Europe are extremely hard to come by. Until a responsible survey is done, as the European Parliament has been requesting for almost ten years now for the EC countries, we can only try to sew together the bits and pieces of information available.

The situation in the Netherlands – one of the rare countries for which such information is available – shows that agricultural production is highly concentrated on just a few crops. Depending on the region, wheat is often sown in rotation with two root crops, sugar beet and potato, while livestock holders grow maize as fodder. This is a reflection of the high level of simplification and specialisation of Dutch agriculture. Graph 3 shows the breakdown of crop coverage in the Netherlands in 1990, whereby a full 80 per cent of Dutch farmlands were sown to merely four crops[27].

Few other data on crop use in Europe are available, but it is likely that the situation in the Netherlands is hardly an exception. Obviously, the fact that European farmers are sowing fewer and fewer crops has a lot to do with the agricultural policies set out in Brussels. Due to Brussels' agricultural price policies, the number of crops on which farmers can (more or less) make a living is shrinking by the day. The main reason why Dutch farmers still include wheat in their farming systems is not so much for the income they derive from it, but rather to ensure a healthy rotation with root crops such as beet and potato. The concentration on fewer crops may further increase under the new directions enshrined in the reform of the Common Agriculture Policy (CAP). More and more

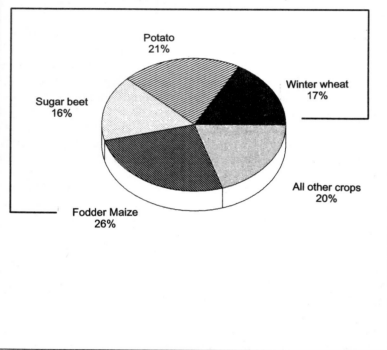

# Crop uniformity in Holland
## The few crops Dutch farmers grow today

*80% of the farmlands sown to 4 crops alone*

Potato
21%

Winter wheat
17%

Sugar beet
16%

All other crops
20%

Fodder Maize
26%

**Graph 3:** Crop uniformity in Holland: the few crops Dutch farmers grow today

agricultural production will be moved to those areas where it is cheapest. We might end up with a situation where the Dutch provide all the milk for the EC, the French the wheat and the Germans the potatoes. On a regional basis, this will certainly further narrow down the variety of crops that farmers are sowing.

## Losing varieties

If data on what crops European farmers are sowing are hard to get, information on the varieties they use is even more difficult to find. Back in 1989, we tried scanning national statistics to draw up some assessment of varietal uniformity in the EC for a study we carried out for the European Commission. We did not have too much luck. The Netherlands traditionally provides the most complete information, as their varietal market is strictly monitored and controlled. The French administration also permanently monitors the seed market, although information is available in a scattered form. For the other European countries, few comprehensive statistics are available so we could only suggest relative trends.

The general picture, however, is devastating. For example, the *Cruciferae* family – including cabbage, cauliflower, radish, turnip, mustard and rape – has traditionally been one of Europe's prime sources of vegetables and oils. Yet the enormous variability of farmers' populations are ceding to the economic attraction of potentially high-yielding F1 hybrids – a one-shot offspring of two parents that yields exceptionally, but only for one generation. An inventory carried out in France in 1986 discovered almost 300 farmer-populations of cauliflower still in cultivation[28]. But many of them were on the verge of being lost as small farmers went out of business. This was particularly the case in Brittany, which along with Italy represents one of Europe's prime centres of genetic diversity in cauliflowers. Yet the biggest irony is that today the bulk of Europe's cauliflower production comes from a few specialised farms in Brittany and Italy, but using a handful of uniform hybrids. A tragic case of squandered wealth, especially since the old genetic complexes often carried important sources of disease resistance. Today's cauliflower grower has to use fungicide sprays to compensate for the lost characteristic.

Among the legumes, edible lupins have a particularly long history in southern Europe. It has been estimated that rural folk in the Balkans selected white lupins for their pigment-inhibiting genes some 4000 years ago[29]. North-eastern Greece – Thrace and Macedonia – has been the scene of severe genetic erosion in this once important pulse crop, mostly due to over-grazing and expanding wheat cultivation. Villagers still remember the old varieties but they are unlocatable today[30]. In Spain, too, the local variation in the white and yellow lupins is on the decline as newly introduced sweet varieties, such as Tremosilla, take over[31]. When the organic farming proponent Philippe Desbrosses commenced his crusade in the early 1980s to rehabilitate the cultivation of blue lupin in the Sologne region of France, the national banks refused him credit. Blue lupin, extremely rich in protein and less bitter than the others, used to be widely cultivated in the Mediterranean for forage and was diversified into many local folk varieties. Today, however, State circles would prefer that innovative European farmers just keep quiet about such adapted alternatives for self-sufficiency in protein crops and continue using Brazil's soya.

In fruits, the replacement of traditional cultivars with more uniform types is rampant throughout Europe. Much of the diversity for stone fruits, nuts, apples and pears is relegated to private family gardens, as market production orchards are mostly sold on mechanical harvesting and synchronised ripening, which is characteristic of modern strains. Today, 93 per cent of France's apple production is assured by a few imported varieties, mainly from North America, of which the Golden Delicious alone represents 71 per cent. Almond production, once a source of pride and a local trademark of Mediterranean Spain and southern France, is almost totally converted there to a few high-yielding varieties from California.

A look at the sparse data of how few varieties of the main crops are dominating the scene in European agriculture provides alarming information. Table 2.6 provides percentages of the crop areas sown to the top varieties of the main crops in the Netherlands. In many crops, Dutch farmers sow close to 90 per cent of their acreage to only three varieties. With the sole exception of fodder maize, at least three-quarters of all major Dutch crops are sown to no more than three cultivars. In some crops, such as spring barley and potato, one single variety dominates over three quarters of the area sown to that crop.

The situation is similar in France. The Office National Inter-professionnel des Céréales (ONIC) is the only body that carries out surveys among farmers to record the varieties in use. The surveys are done at the farmgate level when harvests are delivered to cooperatives, and the data are limited to the main cereals.

The results, reported in Table 2.7, show a somewhat lesser degree of uniformity in France than in the Netherlands, but the uniformity is still impressive. In durum wheat the top two varieties, Cando and Ambral, account for more than 50 per cent of the surface area cultivated. Ten durum wheat cultivars occupy nearly the entire sector (88 per cent). In

**Table 2.6**: Varietal uniformity in the Netherlands (1989)
Percentage of acreage sown to lead cultivars

| Crop | Top variety (%) | Top two (%) | Top three (%) |
|------|------|------|------|
| Winter wheat | 61 | 73 | 79 |
| Spring wheat | 94 | 98 | 99 |
| Spring barley | 76 | 87 | 92 |
| Winter barley | 59 | 71 | 81 |
| Oats | 56 | 74 | 91 |
| Rye | 47 | 83 | 95 |
| Forage peas | 45 | 70 | 93 |
| Fodder maize | 21 | 37 | 53 |
| Sugar beet | 32 | 59 | 77 |
| Potato | 78 | 82 | 84 |

*Source:* Calculated by GRAIN from *Beschrijvende Rassenlijst voor Landbouwgewassen,* Wageningen, 1990.

bread wheat, France's major cereal crop, the top two varieties represent almost a third of production and the top ten just over 70 per cent. The two lead barley cultivars, Plaisant and Express, account for over 42 per cent of the crop while the top ten climb close to the 75 per cent mark.

**Table 2.7**: Varietal uniformity in France (1990)
Percentage of acreage sown to lead cultivars

| Crop | Top variety (%) | Top two (%) | Top three (%) |
|------|------|------|------|
| Durum wheat | 40.59 | 52.58 | 61.20 |
| Bread wheat | 21.90 | 32.27 | 39.38 |
| Barley | 27.05 | 42.75 | 47.75 |

*Source:* Draft ONIC statistics for 1990, provided by ONIC to GRAIN.

In the United Kingdom, the national potato crop is dependent on just a few top-selling varieties. Among the first early varieties sown, the top three cover 68 per cent of area devoted to them. Among the second earlies, the top three claim 71 per cent of the surface. In both of these cases, the number one potato variety covers nearly 40 per cent of the fields planted to this popular tuber. British farmers and gardeners growing potatoes during the main season plant nearly half (49 per cent) of their holdings to just three cultivars[32].

These are alarming figures. French, British and Dutch agriculture depend on just a handful of different crop varieties, many of them genetically not too distinct from each other. There is no reason to believe that the situation in other European countries is substantially different. Again, the data we were able to pull together are scratchy and very incomplete. The following table provides some additional information. The conclusion remains the same. Crop production in Europe is something of a genetic timebomb, destined to explode. The vast sameness plaguing our fields is an open invitation to destruction and disaster. One bug could do it all.

**Table 2.8:** Genetic poverty on the farm in Europe

| | |
|---|---|
| **Wheat** | • More than 90 per cent of the French bread wheat varieties registered and sold to farmers over the past 30 years share at least one common parent in their pedigree; only 9 per cent are truly original types.<br>• Nearly half of the German wheat varieties registered for sale in 1986 derived from the same parent, Caribo. Caribo itself is derived from the French variety Cappelle, one of the top three wheat progenitors used in France. (These top three are found in nearly half the bread wheat seed on the French market.)<br>• The top four varieties cover about two-thirds of the crop's acreage in West Germany through the 1980s.<br>• The top four varieties represent 71 per cent of Britain's winter wheat acreage. |
| **Barley** | • On 3 October 1990, the date of German 'reunification', East German farmers were prohibited from growing varietal mixtures of barley to produce a more uniform product for the West German brewing industry. |
| **Maize** | • In 1986, 60 per cent of the French maize harvest came from five varieties. Of these five, all but one were produced by one firm, France-Maïs, which is owned by the American company Pioneer Hi-Bred. |

|  | • Some 80 per cent of the maize seed produced in France in 1979 had either F7 or F2xF7 as a parent. Both F2 and F7 were created in the 1950s from the folk population Monts de Lacanne. |
|---|---|
| Rye | • In the 1980s, the single variety Halo accounted for half the acreage planted to rye in West Germany. |
| Sunflower | • In the mid-1980s, two varieties, Mirasol and Frankasol, both produced by Cargill, represented more than 50 per cent of France's sunflower production. |
| Potato | • All European potato cultivars derive from two plants brought in in the 15th century. Despite the introduction of wild materials, all cultivated potatoes in Europe carry genetic traces of their common ancestor, Rough Purple Chili.<br>• One variety, Bintje, developed in the 1940s, covers nearly 80 per cent of the potato fields in the Netherlands. |
| Sugar beet | • All cultivated European varieties carry the same genotype for susceptibility to Beet Yellow Virus.<br>• Widespread occurrence of powdery mildew in northwest Europe viewed as a 'timely warning' to broaden genetic variation in this crop.<br>• All European sugar beet hybrids are based on the same source of cytoplasmic male sterility, isolated in the 1940s. |
| Fruits | • Three cultivars make up two-thirds of the newly planted apple crop in Czechoslovakia, replacing most landraces over the past 20 years. |
| Vegetables | • In 1980, more than 1,500 distinctly named varieties were banned from the EC market under the pretext that they were 'synonyms'; independent researchers showed that fewer than 40 per cent were actually different names for the same variety, while more than 60 per cent were originals, simply denigrated by the private sector as not worth the bother to maintain. |

*Source:* Compiled by GRAIN from a range of sources including *Broadening the Genetic Base of Crops* (Pudoc, 1978), P.B. Joly and M.A. Hermitte, *Biotechnologies et Brevets* (CNRA/INRA, 1991), M. Glachant, *La Diversité Biologique Végétale: Elements d'Economie* (CERNA 1991), *Biological Diversity: A Challenge to Science, the Economy and Society* (European Commission FAST Programme, 1987), and various issues of *Semences et Progrès*.

## The legal frames at work

Among the most controversial forces behind the unabating decline of our crop genetic heritage in Europe are the legal and regulatory frameworks that govern activities in the seed sector. There are basically two types of law at work here: those that dictate which seeds can be sold on the market, and those that determine who owns them.

The first set of rules are what we call marketing regulations and they go back to the 1920s, when the breeding sector was starting to organise itself and become a little bit more punchy. The initiative to set up standards for selling seeds came from the profession itself, especially flower and fruit breeders. They wanted to put some order in the marketplace and regulate competition a bit. Government judged it was in the interest of farmers and gardeners to have some measure of quality control on what they were being offered.

From the mid-1920s, the first rules started taking shape all around Europe, providing for the official registration of superior new varieties. The laws date from 1925 in France, 1933 in Germany, 1938 in Austria, and 1941 in the Netherlands. In general, they applied first to the major crops, such as wheat, maize, potato or sugar beet, before being slowly and progressively extended to other crops. Vegetables, in particular those in which the private breeding sector was not too active, usually came last, and some not at all. Asparagus, endive, broccoli, and celeriac are still missing from many European lists. In some countries, such as Austria and Sweden, vegetable species are exempt from mandatory registration. In Switzerland, registration only applies to cereals, maize and potato.

To be registered on a national list and certified for sale, a variety has to fulfil a set of specific criteria. These criteria differ somewhat from country to country in Europe. However they have a common denominator, referred to as the 'DUS' test. To figure on an official list and be legally marketable, a variety must be *distinct*, or distinguishable from all others on the market; it must be *uniform*, that is all the individuals of the variety must be the same; and it has to be *stable*, passing on its salient traits from one generation to the next. In addition, many governments set down further standards for admission on their national list. Most stipulate that the variety show some value for cultivation and use.

The enforcement of the DUS principles and the ruling out of any variety that does not satisfy them, has caused a terrible loss of genetic diversity in our fields and gardens. As they spread from crop to crop, varietal certification laws set extremely rigid standards and marginalised a plethora of varieties, especially those developed by farmers. In particular, the strict demand for uniformity has reduced the diversity commercially available in a given crop for further breeding. Forget about trying to market heterogeneous landraces or an old cultivar. They may be interesting from an ecological perspective or be more adapted to certain farming practices, such as low external input agriculture, but their inherent variability would upset the 'thoroughbred' seed supply. J. Hutchinson, an observer of crop evolution, put it most bluntly when he stated, *'In the European Economic Community we are engaged in making sure that none but the most advanced varieties are allowed to be sold in the area, thereby very greatly restricting the diversity that is available to us.'*[33]

At the same time, these certification schemes narrow down the number of actors who can abide by the rules. Many a creative gardener or non-profit association may take great pleasure in selecting new crop varieties; they may even develop varieties that match the DUS standards. But to pass the certification procedure and get registered on the list costs time and money. Today in the United Kingdom, for example, it costs some $10,000 to register a new variety and keep it on the list for ten years. In France this costs you $40,000. And the fee is the same whether your new variety sells one thousand packets or one million. Obviously, it is not enough to be creative and rigorous to participate in the seed market. You must be rich and pay for the heavy administrative charges – and focus on just a few best-sellers.

### The seed market crash

Everyone seems to remember when stockmarkets crash. And rightly so, after all, when money grows scarce, so will food. But who takes any notice when seed markets crash? Are the effects not similar and probably more long-lasting? June 30 1980 will go down in the history of the EC as the day technocracy triumphed over common sense and the sense of responsibility for plant genetic diversity. That day, the bureaucrats in Brussels deleted from existence more than 1,500 plant varieties from 23 vegetable species. Our crop heritage slashed by the stroke of a pen!

In pure single-market logic, the EC member states decided to amalgamate their national lists into a Common Catalogue and thus create a common seed supply available to all. To be sold in the Community, a variety would have to be registered either on a national list or on the EC list. But the process of amalgamating turned out to be a nightmare. As it was obvious that some varieties were being marketed in different countries under different names, there was a clear interest in rationalising this duplication in the Community. But how to go about it? Growing them all out for some kind of 'genetic sincerity' test would be physically impossible. The European Commission found no other solution than to beg the seed companies to provide a list of what they deemed to be duplicates. The companies eagerly agreed and came up with a 'hit list' of 1,547 vegetables as candidates for deletion.

Gardening and farming organisations grew alarmed when they saw it. The UK-based Henry Doubleday Research Association took a closer look at the list of 'synonyms', and came to a startling conclusion: only 38 per cent of the proposed deletions were actually synonyms for the same variety! Nearly 1000 distinct vegetables were being earmarked for extinction simply because the industry thought of them as unwanted competitors on *their* common seed market. Or in the words of one observer: '*Brussels offered the new seedsmen a golden collective opportunity to not only "rationalize" their own offerings, but also to get rid of the low-profit competition offered by non-hybrid or non-proprietary varieties: Europe's traditional cultivars that belonged to no one.*'[34] The companies and bureaucrats got it their way and with the stroke of a pen a thousand genetically diverse cultivars were written out of commercial existence.

That was 12 years ago and it might happen again soon. Grumblings are being heard again among administrators within national Ministries of Agriculture and the European Commission about the excessive volume of the Common Catalogue. Despite the decline in plant breeders and the rising costs to make it on the list, the number of varieties approved for marketing today has grown to headache proportions once again and the bureaucrats want to cut it down. The question is who will set the guidelines for 'rationalization', how will they be measured and who will be warned in advance of the next crash?

### Staking ownership over seeds

The second body of law governing the seed sector relates to what are called intellectual property rights. Starting in the 1920s, professional breeders in Europe began clamouring for some legal protection of their work. Although plants and animals could not be patented, and the food sector had to be protected from monopolies, they wanted some specific rewards and remuneration for their work. The answer took decades to draw up: a totally special form of intellectual property called Plant Breeders' Rights (PBR). PBR is something like a patent adapted to the world of agriculture: it tries to respect the needs of breeders and farmers alike. Although it provides a form of monopoly control over plants, this

**Table 2.9:** Deleting diversity from the Common Catalogue (1981)

| Crop | Varieties deleted | True duplicates | Unique diversity lost (%) |
|---|---|---|---|
| Beetroot | 57 | 31 | 46 |
| Brussels sprout | 112 | 23 | 79 |
| Cauliflower | 275 | 149 | 46 |
| Celeriac | 5 | 1 | 80 |
| Celery | 41 | 28 | 32 |
| Chard | 11 | 7 | 36 |
| Cucumber | 70 | 10 | 86 |
| Curly kale | 18 | 8 | 56 |
| Endive | 19 | 9 | 53 |
| Gherkin | 21 | 1 | 95 |
| Kohlrabi | 15 | 8 | 47 |
| Leek | 67 | 19 | 70 |
| Lettuce | 1 | 0 | 100 |
| Melon | 36 | 5 | 86 |
| Onion | 137 | 41 | 70 |
| Parsley | 41 | 23 | 44 |
| Radish | 66 | 29 | 56 |
| Red Cabbage | 30 | 21 | 30 |
| Savoy Cabbage | 36 | 27 | 25 |
| Spinach | 76 | 21 | 72 |
| Tomato | 171 | 18 | 89 |
| Turnip | 57 | 24 | 58 |
| White Cabbage | 185 | 88 | 52 |
| TOTAL | 1,547 | 591 | 62 |

*Source:* Based on the European Commission's computerised deletion list as published in Pat Mooney, 'The Law of the Seed', *Development Dialogue*, Dag Hammarskjöld Foundation, Uppsala, 1983, p. 114.

covers only the commercial use of the variety for seed production. The genetic code of the plant itself, and the process of manipulating it, remain part of the inappropriable universe.

Thus, varieties protected by PBR could be freely used by breeders to develop new ones, which is how innovation in plant breeding takes place: you have to improve on an existing variety. At the same time, farmers, now obliged to pay royalties on protected varieties, were assured the right to use their harvest from the crop as new seed. After all, putting aside the best part of the harvest for next year's sowing has been the cornerstone of crop production since agriculture began.

Together, these two derogations – called the breeder's exemption and the farmer's privilege – were meant to guarantee some form of access to genetic resources, which were the building blocks of all further innovations in the agricultural sector. Barricading that access through exclusive monopolies, such as patents provide, would undermine the future of breeding and food production. Or so it was understood in 1961, when a handful of European states signed the International Convention for the Protection of New Varieties of Plants (UPOV Convention). This convention lays down the international principles of PBR and has twenty members today, all from the industrialised world. One of the basic tenets of PBR was that it should be the only form of intellectual property available for plant varieties.

But its total overhaul fell upon us in 1991. With the March 1991 revision of the UPOV Convention, many of the specificities of PBR were eroded, to make it more like a patent right than ever. The ban on double protection was removed, leaving it open for member states to offer both patent *and* PBR protection on plants if they so wish. Further, the farmer's privilege and breeder's exemption have been greatly restricted. If farmers want to reuse seed now, they have to pay additional royalties. And breeders can only freely use other breeders' varieties to create new ones if they make major – not just cosmetic – changes to the plant's genome.

But what effect has PBR had on genetic diversity to date? Again, the viewpoints diverge. Non-governmental organisations concerned with control over plant genetic resources have been arguing for two decades now that PBR does not promote innovation in the breeding sector and reduces the availability of germplasm. By providing incentives to the private sector through guaranteed commercial control over new varieties and royalty payments on seeds, it was assumed that PBR would stimulate a more active breeding industry to the benefit of farmers and consumers alike. By making seeds an attractive investment, we would have more choice offered to us than from an unstimulated, unprotected and hence lethargic public sector. We would get more and better; we would get the fruits of competition.

Unfortunately, none of these promises have been fulfilled. PBR may have stimulated corporate involvement in the seed industry, but that involvement has resulted in there being fewer actors competing on the market. PBR may have promoted the development of more nominal plant varieties on the market, but we have no assurance that there is more genetic diversity among those varieties. Many, if not most, are slight modifications of each other. The concentration of the industry means that the genepool effectively utilised in plant breeding is all the more narrow.

What we can regret most in Europe is the fact that thirty years of plant breeders' rights have done little to promote genetic diversity in our crops and much more to restrict it. While, technically speaking, PBR has represented a liberal 'compromise' regime of access to genetic resources, its impact on the structure of the industry has nullified many potential benefits of this set up. Worse, perhaps, it nudged open the door to the full-fledged patenting of plants and animals.

Patenting life is not a yet a legal reality in Europe, although we are on the precipice. Much will be decided by the fate of the European Commission's proposed directive on the legal protection of biotechnological inventions, which at the time of writing is about to be voted on by the European Parliament – an institution with no power at all against the omnipotent Commission or Council of Ministers.

Of all the implications of this proposal[35], its impact on genetic diversity in Europe will be one of the most profound. Patents will allow for tremendous restrictions on the availability and exchange of genetic resources. Scientists and NGOs will be all the less willing to share their materials for fear they will be (mis)appropriated. Many may even be inclined to join with rather than fight the system, which could bring a final blow to the largely dwindling independence and social accountability of the public agronomic research system. Why should tax payers, starting with farmers, accept this double standard? Farmers, in fact, will be required to pay three taxes on biogenetic research, with no say in its direction: first, to the public research system, heavily exploited and manipulated by private industry; second, on the seeds they buy in the market; and third, for every consequent generation of that patented seed that they reuse. Some varieties of tomorrow may even carry several patents on them for several different genes.

Also, instead of greater variability in crops, we will certainly see biotechnology corporations using the patent system to build economic fortresses around just a few genes or simple genetic constructs: those that code for herbicide tolerance, resistance to antibiotics or insects, longer shelf life. Many of these will be single gene solutions, meaning that they are easily overcome by pests and diseases, making farming a more vulnerable enterprise rather than a more secure one.

These legal frameworks, directing the profit opportunities from research and setting the rules of the market, are perhaps one of the most powerful factors behind the decline of our agricultural diversity and, ultimately, food security. Together, rigid certification rules and strong monopoly rights do everything to keep ordinary people and their local varieties out of the seed supply that should offer alternatives and choices, rather than uniform solutions.

# 3: Genebank or bust

*'In some cases, we may be losing as much diversity in the genebanks as we are in the fields.'*

Participants in the Keystone International Dialogue on Plant Genetic Resources, 1991[1]

The threat of genetic erosion to the future of crop breeding and agriculture itself wasn't recognised until just a few decades ago. European scientists began sensing the problem at the end of the last century, when they realised that farmers' landraces constituted a precious basis for future breeding. The imperative for them was to collect these seeds and get to work on them. Later, in the 1960s, the world at large woke up to the fact that the uniform seeds of the Green Revolution were irreversibly replacing the incredible and unique diversity of local crops where that diversity was strongest, where it originated: in farmers' fields throughout the Third World. This time the imperative was not just to collect what was on its road to extinction but to conserve it indefinitely as a source of options for tomorrow's needs.

Over the decades, the official sector developed a simple method of conserving our genetic heritage: genebanks. And they have banked most of their efforts in this approach to genetic resources management, taking seeds out of the field and putting them away in cold storage. In the past twenty years, though, the technical failings and political problems associated with the genebank system have become increasingly apparent, sparking off a wave of initiatives to mend what is going wrong and also to develop sound alternatives to this single option. Yet, in Europe and elsewhere, we are still a long way from agreeing on the problems and adopting the reforms.

# Banking on diversity

In the early part of this century, a robust and indefatigable Russian botanist by the name of Nikolai Ivanovich Vavilov unfolded a scientific vision that no one could have put together before him. While many 19th-century Europeans wrote and thought about the origins of our crop plants, Vavilov went out to find them. What he found was perhaps not exactly what he was looking for, but infinitely more important.

In 1916, Vavilov went out plant collecting with colleagues in northern Iran, and he did not stop until his arrest back home in 1940 – more than 50 countries and 160,000 seed samples later. These unprecedented ethnobotanical journeys allowed Vavilov to confirm that crops had been domesticated in precise regions of the world, which he called centres of origin. But the real revolution came with his evidence that the eight centres of origin he identified coincided with centres of diversity: geographical pockets of incredible genetic variation within crops. His evidence lay in the mosaic of Afghan and Ethiopian wheats, Peruvian potatoes and Japanese radishes that he and his colleagues amassed over the continents and brought back to the Soviet Union.

The purpose of Vavilov's travels was not idle plant curiosity. It was the practical need to breed better crops for Soviet food production. Most European plant breeders were content to collect and cross already well-adapted local farmers' varieties and some had built up large and representative collections: Vilmorin's wheats in France, Weibullsholm's peas in Sweden, von Proskowitz's barleys in Germany. Vavilov, however, recognised the need to employ an even broader genetic base in breeding programmes. Under his direction from 1920-40, the Institute of Plant Industry at Leningrad became Europe's – indeed the world's – first genebank, and pioneered a whole new approach to crop improvement based on the total genepool of a crop, including weedy relatives and wild species as unique sources of important characteristics. This wider circle of ancestors and relatives of our domesticated crops provided a critical untapped wealth of genes for resistance to disease and pathogens, as well as breeding material to broaden the adaptive range of a crop. The whole world, not just Europe, was to become a treasure chest for plant breeding.

Vavilov's work, and his dedicated mission to collect diversity for the future of agriculture, inspired many European scientists. By the 1930s, Erwin Baur, director of the Institute for Breeding Research near Berlin, was sending out collection missions to South America, Anatolia, the Hindu-Kush, Tibet and Ethiopia. Meanwhile, Jack Hawkes led the

British Empire Collecting Expedition to South America to gather wild potato species in the tuber's centre of origin.

Vavilov's scientific creativity and ruthless energy cost him his life, but may have saved ours. The man who did more than anyone to assemble, study and safeguard a wealth of genetic variation for the long-term needs of food production was arrested in 1940 and died of hunger in a Soviet jail three years later. His genetics, which won him the respect and leadership of scientists throughout the world, were simply not Stalin's. Trofim Lysenko's more Marxist stories about acquired characteristics were far more palatable to the Soviet leader. Why bother with breeding if you can take a summer wheat and grow it in the winter so that it becomes a winter wheat? Plants (and of course people) need not be trapped by the destiny of their genes; they could become whatever experience made of them. So sang Lysenko, much to Stalin's delight. And so sang Stalin to Winston Churchill: *'We have improved the quality of the grain beyond measure. All kinds of grain used to be grown. Now, no one is allowed to grow any sort but the standard Soviet grain from one end of the country to another.'* [2] The dictatorship of uniformity at its best.

Twenty years later, Vavilov's scientific reputation was officially restored but by then it was almost too late. In the 1960s, Vavilov's centres of diversity were shrivelling dramatically under the high yield promises of the Green Revolution. Almost overnight, the rich wheat landraces from Pakistan through Syria were replaced single-handedly by a uniform 'miracle' strain concocted in Mexico. The same was happening to the rices of Asia and maize varieties in Latin America. While genetic erosion had been speeding up alarmingly in Europe over the past 150 years[3], nothing was comparable to the holocaust unleashed in the very cradles of genetic variation. But as pointed out by Christian Lehmann, then Director of the former German Democratic Republic's outstanding genebank at Gatersleben, it was easier now for scientists to ring the alarm bells than in Vavilov's time. Now, people would listen[4].

But it was not so easy after all. Awareness was growing in various circles of the vital importance of genetic resources for plant breeding and the consequent danger of their loss. But the solution turned out to be almost worse than the problem.

The UN Food and Agriculture Organisation (FAO) started taking up work on the matter in the late 1940s and into the 1950s, and organised several major international conferences, one in 1961 and another in 1967, to get the work going on a global scale. During these meetings, the term 'genetic resources' was forged and the sinister map of genetic erosion began to be drawn.

Meanwhile, things started to move at the European level too. The European Association for Research in Plant Breeding (EUCARPIA) started talking about conservation in the 1960s and put forward the idea of creating regional genebanks in Europe. The main concern was to set up storage units linked to the agro-ecological zones in Europe, to conserve the rapidly disappearing landraces and old cultivars. Towards the 1970s several were being established: one in Bari, Italy, for Southern Europe; one in Braunschweig, Germany, for Northwest Europe, and another in Sweden for Scandinavia. Yet none of them except the Nordic Genebank, and to a lesser extent Bari, took up a truly regional function.

This initial regionalist approach to genebanking in Europe evidently had an influence on those concocting a genetic resources strategy for the world at large. In 1971, the Consultative Group on International Agricultural Research (CGIAR) was set up. The CGIAR, housed in the World Bank in Washington, was established to take over the sponsorship of the Green Revolution from its founding engines, the Rockefeller and Ford Foundations. One year later, at the second meeting of the CG's Technical Advisory Committee (TAC), FAO tabled a proposal to set up a global network of genetic resources centres. The big question was how to do it. People linked to FAO advocated the establishment of nine regional genebank centres in major areas of genetic diversity under the control of local governments. The centres would house base collections of materials, for long-term storage, associated with a series of active collections, for immediate breeding and research purposes. The centres would carry out regional strategies for crop improvement and agricultural development based on common agro-ecological criteria – pretty much an extrapolation of the EUCARPIA scheme.

The CGIAR, however, had other plans. In 1974, they created their own genetic resources arm, the International Board for Plant Genetic Resources (IBPGR), and gave it an office (and political autonomy) inside FAO. Over the following years, IBPGR went to work building an empire. Farmers' fields, seed bins and markets throughout the Third World were scoured for local varieties. Genebanks were built, national programmes were set up, and a network of some 40 heavyweight 'base collections' was put together essentially concentrated within the CG-sponsored International Agricultural Research Centres (IARCs) or based in the industrialised countries. This was to be the foundation of food security: storing seeds in far-off locations, reserved for the use of scientists with credentials, rather than letting farmers use and improve them.

To some extent the originally proposed regional networks could not have made more botanical and political sense. They would have allowed countries with common crops and farming systems to work together in a cost-effective manner on relevant conservation and breeding problems. They would also have allowed the regions to build up their technical and political capacities in managing genetic resources in a dignified manner. Yet dignity was clearly not the objective. The main problem with the regional approach as stressed by Cary Fowler and Pat Mooney, was that a regionally oriented and decentralised network would not allow for centralised donor control[5].

It did not take long before the high-tech approach towards centralised gene banking started showing its technical deficiencies. Genebanks have power failures, they are underfunded and often poorly staffed. Genetic diversity is not immutable in cold storage: seeds are under selective pressures, they decompose, they can (and often do) die in storage. Genebanks also often store what a visiting scientist can find during a brief visit to a foreign country. Hence the question of representativeness arises. What is collected may be only a minute fraction of what really exists.

Another major problem with the genebank approach is that we know very little about the varieties stored in them, and even less about their potential uses. Divorced from their agroecological origins, rarely will we have information about the complex interactions of the variety in question with other aspects of the farming system such as the crops they were grown with and rotations they formed part of. In fact, the problem of the lack of knowledge about the material stored in genebanks is so serious that plant breeders hardly ever call on genebanks for new materials. The genebank approach is failing even the formal system itself. Conservation is effectively cut off not only from use in production, but also from improvement through breeding.

Apart from the long list of technical problems, the political discrepancies underlying IBPGR's network became increasingly evident. When, at the turn of the 1980s, a cry of outrage rang out in Third World diplomatic circles at the FAO, it took many outsiders by surprise. The main point of contention: who controlled and, more importantly, who owned the genetic wealth of the developing countries? IBPGR no longer looked like the benign and benevolent IARC it was set up to be in the old Rockefeller style. It looked instead like a rapacious genetic colonialist. Something was quite wrong with the global conservation system it created. Duplicates from collecting missions in many a Third World country were not left behind. Germplasm earmarked for back-up storage in the United States – assumed to provide the most competent and secure genebank system – was being held hostage according to Washington's political considerations. There was no legal certainty as to who ultimately 'owned' the genetic resources held in trust at the IARCs. And most of IBPGR's collections ended up in a few genebanks in the North (the excuse being their great technological capacity to guarantee safe genebanking), which turned out to be less competent or secure than some genebanks in the South.

Aside from the practical and legal uncertainties, IBPGR's investment strategy also looked a bit perverse. Traditionally European countries have been IBPGR's biggest financial donors. Collectively, they provide over half of the board's budget. Yet back in 1981, when they last published such shocking information, IBPGR unabashedly made it clear that a range of European governments were not just donors to but also net recipients from IBPGR. France, the Netherlands and Spain all got money back to support national activities. But Italy and the UK actually received more than they gave! (*Graph 4*)[6].

In short, there was something far too political about this seemingly technical operation. IBPGR's global strategy looked like it was working far more to the benefit of the North than the South. And to make matters worse, developing countries were deeply shocked by the fact that the North was permitting their breeding companies patents or plant breeders' rights on seeds that were developed through the use of Third World germplasm – and sometimes selling them back to the Third World with a premium royalty price attached.

The famous 'seed wars' at FAO attracted years of public attention, as a rather crude saga where the poor were fighting the rich over questions of access to their own botanical wealth and some democratic account-ability to govern the global genebank system. The control and conservation of the Third World's strategic genetic resources acquired great media coverage just at the time that biotechnology was making stockmarkets bounce in the greed for new pay-offs. Genetic diversity was more than a question of food security; it was, clearly, big bucks.

The situation as it stands today is not at all bright. Global control over crop genetic resources stored in genebanks is more concentrated in the hands of the North than ever. In the early 1980s, it was calculated that Third World governments were managing 31 per cent of the world's total germplasm in storage, versus 55 per cent in the North and 14 per cent in the IARCs neatly funded and controlled by the North[7]. A few years later, IBPGR defendants asserted that things were getting better: '*The increase in genebanks in developing countries is significant. IBPGR has sought to redress the former imbalance in germplasm collections when most collections were held by industrial countries. Now, the "South" has become well-endowed with genebanks as well.*'[8]

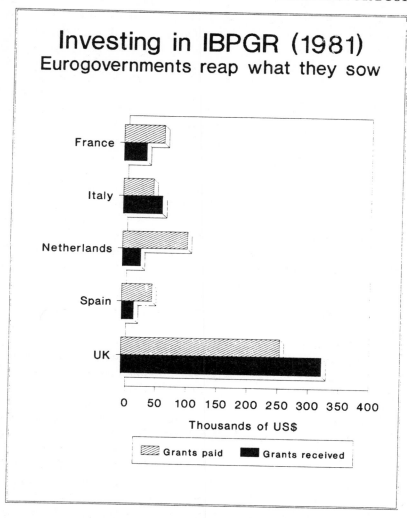

**Graph 4:** Investing in IBPGR: Eurogovernments reap what they sow

The first and last sentences of that quote are quite correct. When IBPGR was founded in 1974, there were eight long-term seed storage units in existence, located in industrialised countries and at a few International Agricultural Research Centres[9]. The developing countries today house a plethora of genebanks; they have sprung up like mushrooms and not just

71

by IBPGR's doing. The Germans built Kenya's unit, the Nordics are launching the Southern African (SADCC) genebank, the Japanese are spending huge sums to construct those in South-east Asia. But what is in all those genebanks and who is running them? For example, IBPGR funded a fantastic genebank in Bangkok with a capacity to store no less than 40,000 accessions. Daycha Siripatra and Witoon Lianchamroon, working with a Thai non-governmental organisation (NGO), report that it presently contains only 2,600 samples, most of them winged bean from Indonesia[10]. Too often, genebanks are set up in developing countries and the donors walk away, leaving no money to run the operation or train the personnel to manage the bank.

On a global scale, the South's share in germplasm management has significantly *eroded* since the early 1980s – according to IBPGR's own statistics: down to 26 per cent from the 31 per cent count in the early 1980s (*Graph 5*)[11]. The 'former imbalance' has not been redressed: in proportionate terms it has grown unmistakably worse. This is not to say that some Third World countries are not running excellent genebanks; some truly are and could serve as an example to many European institutes.

But things may slowly be changing. The last few years have seen growing consensus over some political and technical aspects of genetic resources issues. Following heated debates at FAO about the legitimacy of Plant Breeders' Rights, the international community now recognises Farmers' Rights *'arising from the past, present and future contributions of farmers in conserving, improving, and making available plant genetic resources.'* Meanwhile, IBPGR seems to have become increasingly aware of the role of farmers in conservation and now seems to be going through a form of renaissance under the leadership of its new Director, Geoffrey Hawtin. The 'germplasm traffic cop' – as IBPGR was once labelled, because of the way it directed the flow of genetic resources from South to North – may become a doctor. Some of the staff seem to favour a more integrated approach to conservation that would mend the ills of the current system and try to get it up on its feet. They seem to be starting to recognise that farmers, who after all developed that diversity, have a role in conserving and using it on their farms as well.

Yet while it is one thing to talk about involving farmers in conservation, there still remains the problem of getting the genebank system, so heavily invested in, to function really well. Massive collections of seeds are being held in storage and they might well have been wiped out if they had not been gathered by scientists. But there are two immediate problems. First, the collections are so big that they are hard to manage. And second, they

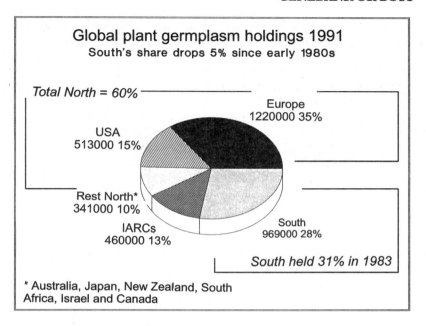

Graph 5: Global plant germplasm holdings 1991: South's share drops 5% since early 1980s

are not getting to the users. On the first matter, IBPGR is promoting the idea of whittling them down to a core subset of the diversity in store and putting the rest in reserve. Yet it is hard to figure out how to sift out this core and there is every risk that the reserve will be dangerously neglected and simply die out. On the problem of use, IBPGR is turning away from promoting central storage units for base collections and to promoting crop networks where certain genebanks liaise on specific crops. This may do very little to strengthen national programmes that work with a broad range of crops and certainly leaves farmers out in the cold.

Despite the controversy inside and outside the system, there is increased recognition that today's almost exclusive reliance on the high-tech genebank approach is technically vulnerable and politically problematic. But there is still a long way from theory to practice. Numerous calls to promote integrated strategies to conserve genetic resources in the farmers' fields and to upgrade the role of farmers organisations and other NGOs in the current conservation system, have until now resulted only in scarce examples of what could be done. No amount of doctoring current ills will amount to much unless govern-

73

ments take their political responsibilities and commitments to genetic resources conservation seriously enough to really make it work.

## From the field to the fridge

How does a genebank or a genetic resources programme work? The idea of a genebank is really quite simple: you dry seeds of a specific plant variety and deposit them into a cold storage unit, with the hope of pulling them out again someday for a useful breeding programme. But the reality is a bit more complex. The cold dark shelves of the bank are only one link in a long chain of never-ending activities that go from collecting the material to the release of a new variety with the salvaged genes in it.

### 1. Getting it in

It may sound easy, but it is not. Collecting genetic diversity can be like trying to find a needle in a haystack. Vavilov set the example: success depends on good maps of plant distribution patterns and endless recording of information. You can either have a precise idea of what you are looking for, such as oats or pumpkins, or simply set out to comb an area rich in diversity but threatened by genetic erosion, like a coastal zone caving in to hotel construction or a river plain about to be dammed. Whatever the target, collecting diversity means scouring everything from the slightest leaf pushing out between two rocks on a rugged hillside to the bins in a creaky attic of an old farmers' house. Most of all, it means talking to people to get precious information on where a plant or tree is from, its history, special name or specific use. After all, the local people are the ones who will have kept the plant variety, cultivated or wild, from dying out.

Not all programmes bother to go even that far. A genebank builds up its stock either by going into the field to collect materials or by acquiring them from another genebank or breeding programme. Most of the collections in the West European system are based on breeders' collections of local landraces that were already assembled in the earlier part of this century. In that sense, with a few exceptions, they are fairly narrow in geographic (and probably genetic) coverage. East European countries, by contrast, have traditionally led a more active collecting strategy, of which the Vavilov Institute's is unsurpassed. In 1990, the Russian institute carried out 40 collecting missions covering 55 regions of the former republics of the USSR, yielding 34,000 new seed accessions. They also went plant hunting in 13 foreign countries, from Ecuador to Vietnam, collecting 7,500 samples[12]. The Gatersleben genebank in the former GDR is another that has carried out a policy of systematically collecting in other countries on a regular, annual basis.

## 2. Storing it away

After collecting, you take the plane back to Berlin or Birmingham and get down to work. The seeds have to be cleaned, dried to a low moisture content and packaged with a label for future reference. For a low-tech working collection, you might get away with storing the seeds in old vodka bottles or paper bags and keeping them in a cool place. Some genebanks still do. According to Cary Fowler and Pat Mooney, who visited Leningrad in 1985 and 1989, the Vavilov Institute's cereal collection there looks more like a wine cellar than a genebank. Sorghums, millets and other small grains are packed away and stored in racks of old wine bottles in the basement[13].

Not so with the fanciest modern base collections for long-term conservation. These are the ones that conjure up the real image of a genebank: cold, grey chambers with steel shelves and hundreds or thousands of jars, boxes and vacuum-sealed aluminium packets or tins. They're basically like walk-in meat lockers adorned with red digital thermometers, electronic humidity controls, back-up generators and plenty of alarms to go off as the temperature rises when you don't shut the door quickly enough. The whole point is to put the seeds to sleep so that they hold still and don't germinate, but without killing them altogether. A tricky business indeed, particularly when you grow them out.

There are essentially two types of collections a genebank can establish: active (or 'working') collections which are stored at +3–5° Celsius, and base collections, for long term storage at a chilly 18–20°C below zero. The purposes of the two are quite distinct. An active or working collection is meant to be just that. The plants are used in daily research and breeding programmes and are often composed of highly uniform, 'advanced' genetic materials, to cater to immediate crop improvement needs. Base collections, by contrast, usually contain a vast range of materials from undomesticated wild species to old cultivars, and are put away for long-term security to face the needs of the future. In that sense, most of the samples in a base collection are not available for distribution or exchange; they're simply put away in storage. Ideally, they should cover the full spectrum of variation for a crop genepool.

The national programme, if there really is one, will usually decide which kind of strategy to pursue for which crop. Of all the collections in the world, about 40 are internationally (IBPGR) recognised base collections, where the genebank accepts global or regional responsibility for a maintaining a certain crop in storage. A range of European institutes participate in this IBPGR network. Responsibility usually results from the country being in an area of diversity for the crop, from a particular economic interest or because the collection was already built up by breeders or scientists in the past. To participate in the network, a genebank must in principle be up to par with IBPGR's technical standards. But this system of commitments is not legally binding: it works on the basis of good faith and trust. To give more weight to these arrangements, the IBPGR register of genebanks participating in the network has been merged into FAO's efforts to set up a global system of base collections as of 1990. Through the FAO network, governments are formally requested to make an international legal commitment to conserve their national germplasm collections[14].

### 3. Keeping them alive

As seeds sit in storage they are dying a slow death. When their germination capacity drops to a certain level, or when there are too few seeds left of the sample for distribution, the accession has to be grown out to produce healthy plants that will provide fresh seed for storage. In both stages, on the shelves and in the grow-out plots, the risk of losing genetic diversity is tremendous. This is particularly true in the case of landraces or populations, which are mixtures of genotypes rather than pure varieties, and doubly true if the seeds were collected from a climate and soil far different from their new home. There is not a lot of research going on with respect to genetic changes during storage in Europe, but the Polish Academy of Sciences has done some studies on their national rye collection – probably the most important in the world – showing that such changes do occur[15].

As to regeneration, the risks of genetic change through unavoidable selective pressures are very well known. Much depends on the crop's reproductive system, grow-out protocols and the quality of storage. Cereals can endure confinement on the shelf for 30 years without experiencing sunlight or rain, but some vegetables bale out much more quickly. The lettuces in the Dutch genebank, for example, have to be checked for viability every eight years. One can speculate about the genetic changes affecting the wild ancestors of our salads when they are cultivated under a slew of pesticides inside greenhouses on Wageningen campus, compared to their original habitat in the Caucasus mountains[16]. Simply put, growing out Iranian lentils in a research station in Siberia is just not quite the same thing as growing them in a farmer's field south of Teheran. Plants evolve, whether in the liberty of a field or in the jail of a genebank unit. What you save is not necessarily what you get.

### 4. Putting them to use

But genebanks – at the least the better ones – don't just store seeds. That would be fairly pointless. For the genetic resources contained in the collections to be of any use as genetic resources, a lot of information has to be compiled about them: when and where they were collected (passport data), the main heritable features of the plant variety (evaluation) and its potential breeding value (characterisation). All of this data has to be put in a computer, organised, updated, and made available to other genebanks, scientists, breeders and researchers by catalogue or computer disk. Otherwise, the seeds just sit there.

To run a genebank properly, you first of all need staff trained in at least some of the following scientific fields: taxonomy and physiology, so that plant varieties can be identified in the field or in the lab for their distinct characteristics; biology and genetics, to describe the plants and evaluate their performance in different environments; documentation and computer sciences to manage databases and get the information out to the user community (plant breeders and researchers). You also need good technicians to manage the collections and grow out seed samples periodically. To put things in perspective, a number of West European programmes (West Germany, UK, Netherlands) have no more than between five and ten scientific staff, while several Eastern programmes like the former GDR and Hungary have/had between 10 and 20. For its part, the Vavilov Institute in Leningrad has (or had) over 100 academically qualified personnel[17].

Because there are so many activities involved, no one institute can afford – and few could possibly manage – to carry out all of the necessary steps independently. International cooperation, for example on collecting missions or evaluation procedures, is often necessary. And a number of national genetic resources centres depend on the collaboration of farmers and breeders to grow out materials to regenerate the seed supply or do some of the evaluation work.

## The Euro 'gene scene'

From a distance, the situation in Europe's genebanks today looks rather bleak. The political restructurings and social instability in places such as the Commonwealth of Independent States, Poland and Yugoslavia have everyone questioning what will happen to their unique germplasm collections and long slaved-upon databases. Bonn's annexation of East Germany in October of 1990 left the staff at the former GDR's Gatersleben genebank nervously wondering whether they would soon be out of a job, and what would happen to their unique collection. The Bulgarian genebank is about to be closed for lack of funds during the transition to a market economy, but the results could be *'irreversible with regard to the* [germplasm] *collection and the staff as well.'*[18] In the UK, germplasm collections never seem to sit still as they are shifted from institution to institution, and sometimes just miss being sold off to the private sector in the name of economic rationality. Meanwhile, over the past year and a half, the EEC genebank directors have been thrashing themselves to get so much as one ECU out of the bureaucracy in Brussels to keep the whole operation alive. No one seems to understand.

But if we start looking inside the system, there is room for hope. Not that the genebanks are all doing a great job, far from it! Many of the seeds stored away in the laboratories of several countries probably would not germinate if you poured champagne on them. Yet against the financial uncertainties and policy changes imposed from above, Europe's formal genetic resources system is being carried forward by a group of highly motivated and dedicated individuals who are really the only basis for optimism.

Europe certainly holds the records for the first, the biggest and some of the best in the world gene scene – but all in East Europe. In fact, many West European genetic resources programmes would rake in only booby prizes if there were an international contest to judge them. Under the list of firsts, the Vavilov Institute sponsored the first global genetic diversity hunts (early 1900s), established the world's first institutional genebank (1920s), and launched the first regional programme for international cooperation on genetic resources through the COMECON network (1964). It is also still the biggest. As to the best, you don't have to have a PhD in genetics to be convinced that the Gatersleben genebank of the former GDR was top notch in a world of mediocracy. Since the end of the war, when the institute was moved from Vienna to its home southwest of Berlin, the Gatersleben people have been doing serious, spirited and high-quality work[19].

Many East European public genetic resources programmes were set up early on: in Czechoslovakia in 1951, Germany in the 1930s, Hungary in the 1950s, and so on. By comparison, while plant breeders and scientists in the West had built up collections of landraces in the early decades of this century, a fair share of that material was either lost during the Second World War or thrown away at the end of a breeding programme. The West's genebanks are quite recent. When Western governments began investing in genebanks in the 1970s, they started with whatever was left. The Federal Republic of Germany's genebank in Braunschweig began operations in 1971, the Nordic genebank was set up in 1979, and the Dutch genebank came into existence as late as 1985.

Some countries have not invested in genebanks at all and are either happy enough to house some dispersed collections within universities or agronomic research institutes, or pretty much look the other way. Several small countries, such as Albania, Luxembourg and the Republic of

Ireland, fall into this category but also some heavyweights, such as France and the UK. There is no genebank in France charged with the responsibility for long-term storage of crop germplasm. Yet France is one of Europe's – and the world's – strongest commercial forces in plant breeding and seed production. As for the UK, there is no national genetic resources programme or policy, and funding from the government has been an uncertain affair for most institutes committed to conserving germplasm. However, a national review was carried out in 1991 and argues for the development of a long-term national programme at last[20].

The structures, histories and politics of the national genetic resources programmes in Europe are quite diverse. As a simplification, there are three types of national approaches to genetic resources in Europe:

1 The centralised approach, with a very clear hierarchy of decision-making and generally one major national genebank;
2 The decentralised approach, often consisting of a nationally coordinated network of collections and research programmes scattered throughout the country;
3 The 'no commitment' approach, where there is no national programme, coordination or genebank.

A very rough breakdown of 25 European countries is given in Table 3.1, showing that the centralised approach is currently the dominant one.

No one country can possible conserve all the genetic resources for all the crops it could possibly want or need, which makes international cooperation so essential. The problem with cooperation, however, is that it demands strong partners, not weak ones. But which comes first, strength or cooperation? Networking should strengthen the participants, but they cannot participate effectively unless they are strong. For example, in the 1970s, a Mediterranean programme of cooperation tried to bring together the national genetic resources programmes of the western Mediterranean basin under the wing of IBPGR. It stumbled along for a few years until it was realised that the imbalance in strength among the programmes was impeding real progress. Italy could play a fine and energetic role, but Portugal and Cyprus were not up to par.

Since 1980, European programmes have been liaising together on a couple of priority crops. The European Cooperative Programme on Plant Genetic Resources (ECP/GR), as it was called, developed crop working groups and crop networks to bring together expert institutes and divide the tasks. Currently, all European countries with genetic resources programmes are participating in the programme except Albania and Romania. While the West puts up the cash, East European

**Table 3.1:** Current structural approaches to genetic resources conservation in Europe

| Centralised | Decentralised | No commitment |
|---|---|---|
| Bulgaria | Austria | Albania[1] |
| FRG | Belgium | Ireland |
| ex-GDR | Cyprus | Luxembourg[2] |
| Greece | Czechoslovakia | Switzerland |
| Italy | France | |
| Netherlands | Hungary | |
| Nordic countries | Portugal | |
| Poland | ex-Yugoslavia[2] | |
| Romania[2] | UK[3] | |
| Spain | | |
| Turkey | | |
| ex-USSR | | |

(1) The country has no cold storage facility.
(2) National genebank under construction.
(3) National strategy and funding commitment under development.

*Source:* For Western Europe, J.J. Hardon, 'Crop Genetic Resources Conservation in Western Europe', 1989. For Eastern Europe, GRAIN's approximation based on IBPGR, *Geneflow*, September 1990.

countries pay in kind and are very dynamic actors in the programme. Activities basically revolve around centralising information into common databases and rationalising collections by identifying duplicates held throughout genebanks in Europe for a few crops, like barley and oats.

### The approach in the East

On the whole, Eastern Europe has put a lot of serious effort into building up its national programmes: conserving, researching and utilising our crop heritage. With hindsight, a certain amount of credit for this is due to the sustained efforts of the Vavilov Institute in maintaining the impetus both at home and in the COMECON network. East Germany's programme and staff were particularly well linked to the breeding community, meaning that genetic resources were actively researched, developed and used to develop new varieties to fulfil farmers' needs. For example, the development and use of varietal mixtures, rather than growing monocultures, was the mark of East German barley production. This effectively kept diseases under control and saved the East German farming community the cost of using chemicals. Gatersleben staff are known for their excellent work in collecting not just seeds but farmers' knowledge about them, and some even wrote cookbooks focusing on wild plants.

Czechoslovakia, Poland and Hungary have consistently worked to document what was out in the field, what was in storage and to maintain their national collections well. In Poland, breeders, rather than scientists, manage the crop collections with the effect that the material is (or was) directed toward its use value. They also excelled in compiling European crop databases. In Hungary, farmers are directly involved in growing out the materials.

In general, the quality of staff, the energy put into information work and the emphasis on building up sound collections and using them well has characterised a number of East European programmes. As a result, those programmes have been larger, more coherent and more genuinely useful than those of the West.

### The approach in the West

Compared to the East, the West seems to have a perverse sense of priorities. Or at least, few West European governments seems to take genetic conservation seriously. Formal commitments to plant genetic resources management exist on paper in a few countries, such as Greece or Scandinavia. Greece, however, lacks the budget to put those words into action. The Nordics are among the few who have taken the matter to heart. France has a National Bureau for Genetic Resources but no policy or coordinated programme. West Germany has a very rigid programme. Their national collection is mainly a working collection, with no emphasis on sampling total genetic variation of the crops, and often not working at all, as interaction with breeders is limited.

It would seem that since they realised the need to conserve genetic diversity for future breeding, many West European governments have put more effort into supporting IBPGR to collect genes in the South than into getting their own houses in order. While it is critical that rich countries participate in the global system, it is equally critical that they get their domestic act together. Altogether, Europe spends more than $4 million a year on IBPGR, covering over half the institute's budget, all in the name of 'promoting the cause'. The EC Member States provide almost three of these four million. By comparison, the same EC countries spend no more than about $6 million on their own conservation work[21]. The United Kingdom has traditionally been the single largest European donor to IBPGR. In 1990, it provided nearly one million dollars to the Rome-based agency. In contrast, the UK government only spends about half a million dollars on its national genetic resources work[22].

## Facing the difference

This East–West contrast was perhaps no more painfully clear than on the day that two genetic resources programmes, Gatersleben's in East Germany and Braunschweig's in the Federal Republic, had to look each other in the face. That was in 1990, the year of 'reunification'. For the first time ever, a joint summer gathering was held between the two genebanks. The celebration, though, was short-lived. On 3 October, when Bonn annexed the five *länder* of the East, Gatersleben's past was erased, and its future suspended. The challenge was to decide how to reorganise things. Braunschweig, with its reputation for being sluggish, meticulous and cut-off from breeders and germplasm donors, was simply no match for Gatersleben, with its large and precious collection, dynamic and motivated staff, good relations with developing countries and excellent output.

The final decision took quite some time – time during which the Gatersleben programme and staff suffered financial and professional uncertainties. In the end, a compromise was reached. The inferior Braunschweig collection will be merged into the Gatersleben genebank. This way, at least 'Gatersleben's pearls', as Christian Lehmann who ran the bank until last year puts it, will be properly conserved under the directorship of Karl Hammer, long-time Gatersleben staffer and well-respected scientist[23]. As a trade-off, the future research agenda will be adjusted to satisfy Bonn's yearning for leadership – not in conservation but in biotechnology.

## Bargaining in Brussels

Lack of political will translates into scarce resources, financial and human. This is nowhere clearer today than in the European Community. In 1986, the European Parliament voted a major resolution to get the EC's genetic diversity conservation act together. It called for an assessment of the apparently grave situation and proposals for action at all levels, from the farm to the genebank. But the EC authorities never batted an eye. Choked for resources from their side, genebank leaders started trying pathetically to get funding from the European Commission to strengthen their inadequate programmes and complement whatever national funding was available. The Commission politely said they only had money to hand out for research, and it had better be biotech. Running a genebank is not research.

At that stage, NGO activists stepped in to help win political support from the democratically elected decision-makers at the Parliament, rather than from the bureaucrats at the Commission. GRAIN and other NGOs exerted pressure, submitted reports and prepared evidence. Together with grassroots conservation groups and opportunistic genebank directors, we explained our cases and participated in public hearings – all in an effort to convince the elected Members of the European Parliament.

And the effort paid off. At the end of 1991, the Parliament solemnly voted into existence a whole new budget line and programme for genetic conservation in Europe. Perhaps most interesting, in its proposal the Parliament stressed that the programme should embrace not only the genebank approach but also on-farm conservation, and should involve not only officials from national programmes but also NGOs. The bureaucrats at the Commission were panicked, since they know nothing about genetic resources and would have no competence in formulating or executing the proposed programme. The governments at Council were afraid that this initiative would arouse public attention and shed a negative light on their agricultural policies and the uniformity they are causing.

The crisis in the European gene scene is an acute one. If and when money becomes available to pump up the failing genebanks, there is likely to be a major conflict of interests between Southern and Eastern Europe. The Mediterranean area houses more genetic diversity than the North, but also has less money to devote to maintaining it. At the same time, the East has better collections that are certainly worth salvaging from budget slashes in a time of political upheaval. Perhaps the irony of this crude competition for first-hand attention to save genebanks is the fact that, at the end of the day, no one really cares. Failing to support conservation, and contributing more to the erosion of agricultural diversity, few governments have any interest in creating social awareness of the issue.

But the real problem is not the technology, the research and coordination, or the money. Those are just tools, and can be made available or not depending on who sets the agenda. The European Parliament's initiative has made that perfectly clear. The real problem is the social and political legitimacy of genetic conservation: what to do, how to do it, who should do it and for whose benefit. To some extent, the genebank officials themselves have to share some blame for this. For too long now, genebanks have been working almost in secret, and certainly outside the scrutiny of the people who are supposed to depend on them for long-term maintenance of our genetic resource base. As we will see later, NGOs, knowing the gaps and needs at the local level and trying to fill them in, have also been working in isolation and cut off from any support or recognition. Meanwhile, industry has been sitting on the side, oblivious of the whole matter.

This social and political vacuum within which conservation is being pursued, more for the worse than for the better, is by far the largest barrier to truly effective action. Genetic resources carry not only an economic premium that governments and industry must recognise and pay for, but a political premium that calls for consultation and concerted action. Genebanks are not the only option. We have obviously steered too far in one direction and will have to get back on the right track. But for this to work, society at large must be informed of the choices and help formulate the solution.

## Of numbers and nonsense

Those whose job it is to know about these things, tell us that there are about three and a half million seed samples in storage in the world today, a few more than a million of them in Europe (*see Annex 1*)[24]. This sounds impressive, and to a certain extent it is. But don't be deluded by the numbers, or led into a false sense of security. The real picture of the genes in the bank has to be painted on the basis of the job being done: whether the seeds are alive, safe, documented and available, and whether we are really talking about conserving diversity or uniformity. Unfortunately, we do not have all that much information at our disposal. A look at what we were able to uncover on how well the job is being done on the European gene scene is not very convincing.

### Is it alive?

Good question. What good is a genebank full of dead seeds? This is one preoccupation IBPGR does not bother with when sending out question-naires to genebank curators. Of course, even if IBPGR asked, some people might twist the facts to look good. But it is also the most essential question to ask if we are to believe that genebanks are actually making a contribution to the conservation of our plant heritage. No one really has the answer. We can make assumptions but little more.

Many doubts have been expressed, for example, about the viability of Russia's massive collection, which may be more 'PR' than 'PGR'. Nearly half of the collection was put together in Vavilov's time, more than 50 years ago. These are by now rather old seeds, which have had to survive a range of threats to their existence – from the siege of Leningrad to the dissolution of the Soviet Union. As Pat Mooney of RAFI put it recently, *'There is a major gap between data and reality for Russia.'*[25]

Seeds are subject not just to physical threats and shifting political programmes or priorities, but also to the vagaries of available funding. Where national programmes are weak and genetic erosion strong, IBPGR sometimes comes to the rescue. Yet the rescue can be short-lived. In Greece, for example, IBPGR supported some emergency collecting of forage and pasture crops twice in the 1980s. They were under threat from over-grazing, fire and the spread of urbanisation. But today, breeders at the Fodder Crops and Pastures Institute in Larissa warn us not to trust the numbers of samples being stored in their genebank. Why? Helen Ronsiotou, who works at the Institute, is perfectly honest about it. *'Some samples are not alive.'*[26] Funding shortages and the sheer challenge involved in managing diversity can lead to reduced activities in regenerating samples, meaning that they risk dying on the shelves.

Still, short of asking every genebank official for a health check on every sample in their collections, it is virtually impossible today to judge whether the seeds held in storage for the future are dead or alive. IBPGR staff put it quite bluntly: *'Many of the samples may have dead seeds or the holders may lack the funds to regenerate them before the total loss of their viability.'*[27] Genetic diversity is a vital resource, in every sense of the word. Yet the vitality of our government collections has a giant question mark over it.

## Is it diversity?

Another central concern regards how much variation is held within genebank collections. There is a big difference between maintaining an old landrace or wild sample of wheat on the one hand, and a breeders' line or mutant strain on the other. Wild forms are usually excellent and unique sources of resistance to diseases, insects and environmental pressures like drought or salty water. The same holds for landraces, which are generally well adapted to a specific region, climates and soils, and are often hardier and more tolerant of stress than modern varieties. First-hand breeding material, by contrast, is usually very low in diversity and very similar across the crop profile. Different types of breeders' lines may make a difference between a few days before maturation or a little more resistance to cold, but beyond that they are of meagre interest to long-term problems of plant breeding.

Wild relatives of crops might be the best source of disease resistance genes, but they are also the most poorly represented types of seed in our government genebanks. Worldwide, wild species typically account for less than 2 per cent of genebank accessions[28]. Most of Western Europe's collections are made up of whatever landraces had not been lost and a slew of advanced breeding material. In Eastern Europe, larger amounts of old farmers' varieties tend to be conserved, but their collections also seem to be filling up quickly with modern materials. Czechoslovakia has practiced an active policy of importing advanced germplasm from the West for some years. Their thinking seems to be that the elite germplasm will be more useful to raise yields and is a better investment than the old varieties. Russia too is keen on acquiring what is perceived to be the advances of industrial farming.

Some people are starting to complain about this. Polish genebank staff point out that the overload of homogenous breeding material – as opposed to more diverse farmer-bred populations – is a prime disadvantage of their national system today[29]. They and other East European colleagues fear the impact of the new market economy on their genetic resources systems. As privatisation intensifies, short-term immediate needs will dominate longer term strategic action, as is already the case in the West, which means that more emphasis may be put on breeding uniformity rather than conserving diversity.

Big numbers can also hide the reality of redundancy. To what extent the European collections are duplicates of each other is widely unknown, and this bothers genebank staff quite a bit. Obviously there is useful duplication where materials are being held as a safety service for other countries. But there is a lot of useless duplication as well. Nobody really knows how much, though. Some research efforts on specific crops earmarked as a priority in Europe point to a substantial degree of duplication. For example, well over half of Europe's total barley and pea collections, or 60 per cent to 70 per cent, is duplicate material. Up to 20 per cent of Europe's beet samples are probably identical copies of the same varieties[30]. Such duplication is of little credit to the range of diversity that could really be conserved instead.

## Is it documented?

For genebank collections to be of any value to users – breeders, farmers, researchers and industrialists – it is absolutely necessary to develop and provide information about the samples. It is senseless to salvage a disappearing garden bean, dump it in cold storage and walk away. The interest society has in that bean is its past (where it came from and how it was used), its present (where and how it grows best, its characteristics, taste, strengths and weaknesses) and its future (the genes it harbours for improving other beans or other crops, its potential for future farming or gardening needs). Only if this information is compiled and computed can genebank collections possibly serve a useful purpose.

However, basic information on the samples, known as passport data, is available for only half of the seeds in storage. This is very rudimentary information: where the sample is from, its name, the colour of the fruit, etc. The next type of information necessary concerns the characteristics of the varieties: the major traits that express themselves regardless of the effects of the environment. Documenting these basics is considered the vocation of a genebank, like cataloguing a library. Little of it is being systematically done, however. The third level of information, the result of evaluation trials, gives an estimate of how the sample could be used in breeding programmes. There is quite some controversy as to whether impartial genebanks or biased breeders should do this work, as it imposes a heavy value judgement on the germplasm.

In general, documentation is an important gap that restricts the value of current crop conservation work. There is not enough known about the collections and the information registered is not available in an accessible form, a heavy drawback to putting all these seeds into breeding and farming use.

## Is it available?

If the germplasm is there, alive, safe and documented, is it accessible to those who want to use it? Availability relies on two things: that there are enough seeds of a sample to satisfy requests and that there are no policy restrictions inhibiting access to a genebank's collection.

The first factor is purely technical. It supposes that a genebank has enough resources (financial, human and physical) to maintain a supply of seeds for distribution. This is not always the case, of course, and many demands will be turned down for sheer lack of material.

The second depends on the attitudes assumed by genebank directors or the government employing them. Some genebanks, like FAL in Braunschweig, Germany, practice a policy of *quid pro quo* access to their collection. They will make samples available to others on the basis of reciprocity[31]. Former Yugoslavia makes access *'possible under contractual arrangements.'*[32] Yet others earmark certain collections as restricted because the crop is of particular importance to national agricultural development. For example, Turkey restricts the availability of tobacco, fig, grape, hazelnut and pistachio[33]. Other countries are more wishy-washy. It is Finland's policy that *'There are practically no restrictions on access to samples of genetic resources.'*[34] Yet Finland is the European country that earmarks the largest portion of its germplasm collection as restricted – 78 per cent, according to IBPGR's databases. Romania stipulates that landraces and obsolete varieties are freely available, but is silent on wild species and advanced material[35].

All factors taken into account, and still according to IBPGR's databases, six European countries are on record for restricting the availability of more than 10 per cent of their national holdings. Another dozen limit access to a smaller extent. These practices run up against the fine words about 'free access to genetic resources' laid down in the International Undertaking on Plant Genetic Resources, to which virtually all European countries are formal signatories. Such access will increasingly erode if European countries adopt new laws to extend the patent system to life forms, including genetic resources. Many genebank officials have started to worry openly about this. Jaap Hardon of the Dutch genebank doesn't mince his words. *'Patenting genes completely undermines the basic principle of free exchange of genetic resources.'*[36] He and other genebank officials have reason to worry. Just imagine the practical problems involved in finding out which genes in your collection have been patented and advising anyone who requests a sample about the limitations that this might entail for the use of that sample.

### Is it being used?

There is a general perception in the air today that genebanks are hardly used at all by breeders and scientists, much less by ordinary people involved in gardening or farming organisations, local research or rural development. For decades now, critics within the system have been arguing that genebanks are more like museums or morgues than institutions where seeds are deposited for withdrawal and circulation.

The level of controversy over the issue of utilisation of genebank collections is amazingly high, as if all those seeds were a curse and a burden rather than a treasure of immense proportions. To some, it is *mainly* a problem of proportions. There are so many genebanks holding so many accessions that the system cannot be managed effectively and put to good use. To others, the fault lies with the breeders who are only interested in developing one or two top-selling varieties based on their own materials. Yet according to many breeders, the fault lies with the genebanks, which do not characterise their collections, document them and make better known what they have to offer.

A lot of all this has to do with politics. Up until now, for example, genebanks in the EC have been discouraged from working with any great creativity on wheat, because Brussels tells them that it is a surplus crop. Miguel Mota, who runs the Portuguese genebank at Oeiras, finds this ridiculous. He would like to invest efforts in conserving and developing wheat stocks that need less artificial fertilisers and pesticides, but the bureaucrats won't hear of such a venture[37]. The same holds in Italy. Pietro Perrino, head of the Bari genebank, would also like to promote low-input agriculture through adapted genotypes. He is trying to move ahead and work with farmers on developing the cultivation of spelt wheat, as opposed to bread or durum types, because it is hardier and can earn farmers a better income. But the new price policies from Brussels will hardly sanction this alternative. The director of the Spanish genebank laughs cynically about it. Sure, he is trying to manage a massive collection in Madrid but, he snorts, no one is Spain is doing plant breeding! Nobody ever will, if it depends on Brussels' policies.

With the reform of the EC's Common Agricultural Policy, northwest Europe is where the farming action will be, and where investments in agriculture will be promoted. But even there, genebank directors complain about the non-use of their materials. In their countries, plant breeding and agricultural research is fast being privatised and concentrated under the control of a decreasing number of companies, many with their own competitive germplasm stocks of elite and uniform materials. Few of them are looking to genebanks for materials.

The direct danger associated with non-use of germplasm collections is that, if not called upon to foster and serve sustainable development, they could end up in the waste basket. This is a direct threat to us because we entirely depend on the long-term availability of genetic diversity for our future food and environmental security. The price we have been paying over the past decades for the loss of genetic diversity in our agricultural systems is manifest: ever more toxic chemicals to fend off the problems our crops, and mechanised monocultures, are now intrinsically vulnerable to, be they pests, disease, soil erosion, acid rain or climate change. Breeding more sustainable options back into our seeds, livestock and farming systems will be impossible without a broad genetic pool to tap into.

# 4: Salvaging in silence

*We, as grassroots seed savers, are not merely in this for the science [...], we are cultural ambassadors through our seeds, which are living metaphors and links to the earth.*

Gary Paul Nabhan, Native Seeds/SEARCH, 1991[1]

In May of 1991, a group of people attending a European meeting on regional development were visiting a farm in Euskadi and saw that the farmer had some unusual pigs munching away on the grass. It was a very old race that had virtually disappeared from the Basque hills, but this farmer kept breeding a few because they were exceptionally well adapted to the local climate and, quite simply, never got sick. The visitors were surprised, in a positive way, to find someone resisting the push towards uniformity that is penetrating the Basque countryside. As farmers in the region often say, *'Spain did not enter the Common Market. The Common Market entered Spain.'* Still, the farmer's decision to stick to his own traditional breed might pay off . . . to the pork industry in the North. That same year a disease was spreading among pigs in the factory farms of Northern Europe, a disease to which his unique Basque herd was resistant. Now, government officials were calling on him to hand over some of his pigs for crossing with the vulnerable breeds up North, to save the pork industry there.

Two months later, in July, a colleague working with grassroots seed savers organisations in Germany brought us a package of *Mangold* seed from East Germany. Mangold belongs to the beet family, which originated in the Mediterranean. Over the centuries, people selected it to produce edible green leaves above ground, rather than a beetroot underground. Hence, it's name in English: spinach beet. Today, with the rationalisation of almost everything in the former German Democratic Republic, old plant varieties are being quickly taken off the market, to pave the way for West German seeds. Our friend had just been visiting the Gatersleben genebank where the staff were anxiously giving away the now non-listed seeds for free – with the hope that some people would multiply them, share them and enjoy their robust qualities. In fact, we tried them ourselves and despite the very heavy frosts in the mountains of Catalonia this winter, the *Mangold* fared exceptionally well. And as it is more tender than the big chards it so closely resembles and has a very good taste, the vegetable is becoming popular again in countries such as Switzerland and Germany. Were it not for motivated amateurs like Germany's seed saving groups, who rescue old varieties when they are dropped from commercial catalogues or national lists, consumers might have lost yet another option.

As summer waned into autumn, British consumers were offered a curious 'new' product at the supermarket: tomatoes that were labelled *'Grown for taste, not for appearance.'* The industrialisation of British agriculture has meant that tomatoes are now genetically programmed to be hard as rocks (to survive mechanical harvesting and shipping), uniform in size (to fit neatly in a standard box), and slow-maturing (so that they last longer on the supermarket shelves). Things like nutrition, flavour and texture are simply out of the breeding picture, especially if they can be artificially added later on in the food chain. So when innovative supermarket chains decided to offer consumers a decent tomato, the place to look for it was not in the government genebanks or seed industry collections, but in the living backyard laboratories of amateur British gardeners. For what PhD geneticist would save an old tomato variety under the category 'tasty' or 'juicy' or 'great for salads'? That's what ordinary people do.

The availability of one hardy pig, a frost-resistant *Mangold* plant or an exceptional old-style tomato may not spell the difference between life and death for most European farmers or consumers. It could, however, provide important options in how animals are raised, how crops are grown and how appetising or nutritious our food is. But not only do these diverse breeds offer a key to that future, they also bear a record of our past as they have been handed down to us from generations of farmers and gardeners. Somehow, if people like that Basque farmer, the German seed savers, dedicated British gardeners and many others are putting any effort into maintaining this diversity, it must be for a reason. And it must be for a good reason, because caring for those plants and animals not only costs time and money; it is also a hell of a lot of work.

Seed-saving, like crop breeding, has always been a matter of survival. Farmers and gardeners routinely kept part of their harvest for next year's sowing, and in the process of selecting and experimenting, they developed specific varieties that suited their needs or desires. Conservation was not an isolated activity in itself. It didn't have to be. It was part and parcel of producing and eating.

Today things are not much different. We still need to eat and we still need to produce. The question is what and how. A large part of the answer will still be found in the seeds. In fact, conserving plant varieties has never been as much a matter of survival as it is today. Agriculture and the massive standardisation of our food system has destroyed more diversity – and more farmers – in the past few decades than ever before. We not only depend on those plants and growers that are left in order to survive, but their increasingly fragile existence also depends on us.

By and large what we are facing, and what more and more people are struggling against from the bottom up, is the wholesale alienation of diversity from the very fabric of society. This is no aesthetic problem, nor intellectual distraction. Diversity is one of the most potent forces for social, ecological and economic stability. It is the only chance for 'other' to provide an alternative to the 'one' when that one no longer satisfies us or works correctly. And just as diversity was born of the grassroots, of people's creativity and common sense, so too do we have to look to the grassroots for its sustenance and future. Many Europeans have been coaxed into a blind dependence on government and industry to run the food machine – and our societies. But their eyes are beginning to open.

## Conservation at the grassroots

Frankly, it is quite impossible to sum up the logic and spirit of all the different people working to save and use genetic diversity at the local level in Europe. In fact, we can barely capture a fraction of their efforts. Nor do we want to romanticise them and tell quaint stories about fearless underdogs or downtrodden victims of some anti-diversity stampede. But, consciously or not, they are contributing an untold effort to the management of our plant genetic heritage. The point is that it is high time we opened our eyes and looked at what people are doing to conserve and use old varieties. For if they are doing it, there is a reason for it. And given the state of our government-run conservation systems, no one – aside from a few bureaucrats in Brussels whom we know too painfully

**93**

well – could be foolish enough not to take an interest in any other alternative.

It is impossible to say who in Europe caught on first to the need to take a more structured and systematic approach to safeguarding our vanishing genetic heritage at the grassroots level. Until about twenty or thirty years ago, people took seed saving for granted. Anyone who grew anything saved seeds. One thing is for certain, though: the impetus to act against the high tides of genetic erosion came from folks who had a different vision of agriculture than the one being taught in the universities and sold by the chemical companies after the Second World War. The seed savers understood complexity as something you work with in order to work for you, not as an obstacle to some perfectly commandable push-button progress. To them, diversity was a strategy and a source of security that hybrids, artificial fertilisers and pesticides could never match in a long-term perspective.

Small-scale 'organic' or 'biological' farming and gardening had been the only thing around until the bigotry of chemicals, capital and government policies made them the barely tolerable exception. The formalisation of various movements, especially in the 1950s and 1960s, became a necessity in order to win the right to exist and move forward. Despite their differences and some of the nearly fratricidal wars of religion between various schools of eco-farming, biological diversity was part and parcel of every approach. But it took some visionaries to look beyond what was happening in their own backyards and really measure the scale of genetic erosion throughout Europe.

Like the white-coated scientists who rushed in the 1960s to build genebanks to store seeds on the verge of extinction, the folks that took concerted action at the local level were pretty much moved by the same feeling: shock and alarm. One of those people was Lawrence Hills, an eccentric British gardener whose passion was to produce food without poisons. In the late 1960s and into the 1970s, Hills became increasingly concerned about the effects that monopoly laws – in the form of Plant Breeders' Rights – were having on the diversity of the seed supply. He later realised that pending EC legislation to establish the Common Catalogue of varieties that could be sold would spell doom for local genetic diversity. His rapid research into the varieties the EC was about to delete from legality confirmed his fears: more than a thousand folk varieties in Europe were about to be signed out of existence (see page 61)

Hills was outraged. He campaigned in newspapers and on the radio to alert people to the impending holocaust. His organisation, the Henry Doubleday Research Association, started systematically collecting vege-

94

table seeds that were about to be dropped from commercial lists and established a living seed library in 1975. Hills wrote pamphlets and articles and talked directly to gardeners throughout the UK to make a special effort to conserve old varieties. He talked to everyone and anyone, even the British government. The government didn't listen, however, and while various organisations slowly pondered their response, the seed companies destroyed their stocks. Eventually, in 1980, Britain's biggest food charity, OXFAM, gave £10,000 to establish the first UK vegetable genebank as an outright emergency effort. Had the relatively trifling sum been available more rapidly, many more varieties would have been saved.

The development and organisation of what today we call the 'informal sector' started taking shape all over Europe through the 1970s and into the 1980s. There was a whole range of factors that motivated people into putting some systematic effort into collecting, testing, selecting, multiplying and circulating seeds of now rare varieties.

First and foremost was a reaction against what was happening in the market: not only the supermarket, but also the crop 'improvement' market. Plant breeding can dictate where agriculture is going. With the demise of local breeding operations, people were at a loss for varieties adapted to their regions. They also found themselves up against a new seed supply burgeoning with so-called high-yielding varieties that, in reality, had a lot of drawbacks. The high-yields were biased towards one kind of farming system: intense monocultures and the heavy use of chemicals. The chemical and yield bias in modern plant breeding drove many folk to look energetically at other seeds as a basis for more ecologically sound farming and gardening. By recovering and regenerating regionally-adapted, open-pollinated varieties and integrating them into their farming systems, they started a new struggle to regain the fertility of soils and plants and develop a more secure environment for food production.

Another factor that gave people the impetus to collect and save seeds with new vigour and consciousness was the legislation governing the seed market. The legal requirement to be registered on a national list in order to sell varieties and the introduction of Plant Breeders' Rights became important concerns to many groups and individuals. Many seed saving groups practice an explicit policy of monitoring the varieties that are about to be dropped from national lists, and take it upon themselves to salvage those seeds from extinction. In some cases, the absurdity of the law drove local groups to acts of civil disobedience. In Germany, associations began packaging and selling traditional varieties with the words *'For test purposes'*, in order to slip through the net of the law. In

France, family seed companies that had made a living from folk varieties that were now outlawed by the new legislation went into negotiations to establish a professional union to fight for their lives. Last year, NGOs in Spain launched an appeal to promote the farmer-to-farmer seed exchange networks that have broken down with the industrialisation of Spanish agriculture. These NGOs are trying to reinstate diversity and stability into Spanish farming through the use of indigenous varieties that are being lost from the land and ill-conserved in the government genebank. As they put it, *'The institutions are not pulling the cart'* and they feel that they have to[2].

When the motivation does not come from these 'macro' problems, it often comes from the simple observation that the old varieties are disappearing and a desire to do something at the local level. The effect can be amazing. André Hatesse, a private individual in Argenteuil, France, noticed that the botanical assets of local gardens were increasingly diminishing and in 1975 started actively looking around for vegetables that were fast becoming rare. In a couple of years he managed to collect more than a hundred tomato varieties, thirty squashes, fifteen types of radish, a dozen lettuces and so on. According to Hatesse, none of these varieties could be found in any commercial seed catalogue[3]. As France does not have a national genebank with the mandate to conserve vegetable diversity for the future, they might in fact not have been saved anywhere else.

Fruits and ornamentals have often received most popular attention. Various apple-saving movements throughout Europe have enjoyed tremendous success, involving all ages from school children to older village folk, who are usually the last remaining source of information about regional stocks. Even artists have taken action on this front. Tonino Guerra, poet and screenwriter for the film director Federico Fellini, set up a private conservation centre called 'The Orchard of Forgotten Fruits' in Pennabilli, Italy.

Actually, there is such a breadth of different energies and motivations guiding this kind of local action that it is really hard to put forward any exhaustive or singular description of what is going on. Nor would we want to. After all, people save diversity for a diversity of reasons, and that is as it should be. The fact of the matter is that this work is being carried out through sheer will and commitment, with little if any external support. Because these groups and individuals are operating outside the institutional sphere of genetic resources work, we tend to refer to them as the life blood of the 'informal' sector. No one really likes this term, however, because of its many negative connotations. Informal does not mean unorganised. Nor does it mean that these people are not serious or scientific. It refers to the mass of people working outside of the official sector, mostly at the grassroots level, sometimes (but not always) with a different approach to science than the dominant one, and very often much more serious, motivated and committed than those working within the 'formal' circles.

In fact, there is probably only one – and that overwhelming – common denominator characterising genetic resources work at the grassroots level: while genebanks, as we tried to explain earlier, conserve *for* utilisation, people conserve *through* utilisation.

Nowadays, policy makers break up the world of conservation strategies into two categories, *ex situ* ('off site') and *in situ* ('on site'). *Ex situ* generally refers to the genebank approach, which can mean seeds are frozen, put to sleep in liquid nitrogen, kept in glass tubes or sit perched in a field far from where they originated. *In situ* generally refers to nature parks and reserves, where whole tracts of land are cut off from people and agriculture to preserve an ecosystem and its wild inhabitants. But grassroots conservation is starting to make a mess of this neat duality. As more people become voluntarily involved in saving genetic resources from erosion at the local level, and as official circles slowly start to take note of it, this third approach – entrenched in production – has to fit in somewhere. Or does it?

However they are organised, probably all the modern seed savers are in it, in part, for the sheer pleasure of taking care of the seeds, enjoying the harvest at home and sharing it with others to keep the links between plants, people and cultures alive. We recently joined in a visit to NGOs conserving local genetic resources in the southeast of France and were proudly served a copious lunch that included a bounty of wild salad greens with Jerusalem artichokes, spinach beet omelette and platters of La Negresse, 'local' blue potatoes boiled in their skins[4]. The meal gave us quite a lot to talk about! The elders at the table explained how, during the war, there was little to eat in France except those knobby Jerusalem artichokes. The younger people talked about what the potatoes meant to small farmers they recently visited in Latin America. Diversity has to be enjoyed, as stories have to be told, or it dies out.

One of the strategic approaches taken by peoples' organisations that care about diversity is to maintain old and rare varieties for their social and ecological value: hardiness, resistances, staggered harvest, adaptation, role in farming systems, nutritional qualities or fertility. This is especially the case among organic farmers' networks, NGO research organisations and regional development programmes. These groups are highly organised and quite conscious of the fact that they are building an alternative route to conservation and local agricultural development than the one preached or practised by their governments. And in so doing, they are developing different approaches to research – based on other assumptions and goals – than those that fit into today's dominant system.

Sometimes the institutions and administrators look down on seed savers as naive, unprofessional or even dangerous. Especially when they practise approaches to science that do not match the criteria of commercial interests. One night over a dinner in Rome in April 1991, we ventured to ask the UK's National Plant Genetic Resources Coordinator whether he considered the Coventry-based HDRA, maintaining old vegetables for sustainable forms of agriculture, as some sort of enemy. Doubtful of our question, his answer was a straightforward and resounding yes, for their research work is a direct menace to what the government is promoting: chemicals and high yields. Over in France, several NGO programmes to conserve and utilise local genetic resources put highest emphasis on the cultural value of seeds. To them, the issue is not so much germ plasm but people's knowledge and understanding of crops, or what has been called ethnobotany. The State officials scratch their heads. How do you get this folklore stuff into a computer?

Empirical, popular, subjective – all of these terms are used to denounce and push aside the scientific research of grassroots organisations working with genetic diversity. Biodynamic breeding and permaculture are probably the most ferocious examples of this. Biodynamic crop development revolves around one central force: vitality. Their major bone of contention against modern seeds is that they have degenerated: their energy level is low because people handling them today do so without care. Biodynamic breeding tries to reawaken and revitalise that lost energy – and it works *(see page 103)*. Research carried out by groups in Germany and Switzerland, the two fiefdoms of biodynamic seed production in Europe today, have resulted in increased crop fertility and vigour, by paying attention to plants' energy cycles rather than doping them with hormones and fertilisers. Scientists admit that this is logical and admire the audacious creativity of these people, but none the less look the other way.

Thus, many of these groups are not only perpetuating the old types and promoting their use and reinstatement in local farming and gardening, but also carrying out innovative research on cultivation techniques, cropping systems and breeding. The point for them is to encourage and work with the complexity of biological factors in a farming system. The net result is yield stability, improved plant and soil health, and greater nutritional quality of the food. What really counts in their activities is to work with farmers and gardeners to pick up sustainable practices again so that they can adjust and reproduce them on their own holdings, enjoy the benefits and pass them on.

Although some are more dynamic and explicit than others, almost all of these groups are busy advancing what we call regional development: salvaging, maintaining and enhancing local resources for sustainable economic growth. 'Growth' shouldn't be understood here in the hollow sense of 'more, more and ever more'. That logic, while capable of providing tangible outputs in the short term, often ends up destroying far more than it creates. Sustainable growth has to fit into a long-term perspective of permanent regeneration. This is why local development strategies are eminently conservationist, not because they freeze or preserve, but because they rehabilitate and maintain the reproductive capacity of resources – whether they be genetic or cultural – so that evolution and change can persist and be enriched.

This is the broader logic of genetic resources management at the local level. If it sounds a bit fuzzy, that is because it is still underdeveloped and has not been given a fair chance to prove itself. Grassroots conservation NGOs, seed savers and organic farming networks are often cut off from each other, each of them digging into their work in isolation. But they are not just scratching soil. They are involved in the full scope of their surroundings, picking up the pieces of relationships between people, soils, plants, insects and animals that have been fractured and separated, and relationships between the elements of an interactive farming system, between producers and consumers, between culture and agriculture. For they know that emphasising one element over another is a vain and ultimately destructive enterprise. Development has to be holistic or it will not be.

## Salvaging in silence

### Enter the Court of Eden

Contrasts, like diversity, can be very potent. They feed the imagination and open up new spaces to move within. The Dutch genebank in Wageningen is not an unpleasant place to visit. Their collection is small for one of the top breeding countries of Western Europe – some 25,000 holdings of lettuces, spinach, cabbage-related crops and cereals – but their staff team is full of youthful energy and good spirits to make the best of it. Budget cuts mean that, in their new surroundings where all the Dutch plant research agencies are stuffed together, coffee is available for only 15 minutes a day, first in the morning and then after lunch. But they take it in their stride with a healthy dose of humour. They have to, for they know that the important thing is to run a respectable genebank.

Just a 20 minute train ride from the white walls, high-tech seed storage units and widespread multiplication fields of Wageningen is the urban bustle of Utrecht. Who would believe that just behind the central railway station is the Court of Eden: a tiny, four-storey house filled with more seeds from more countries in the world than the government's glossy genebank 40 kilometres east. Gus Lieberwerth is only 30 years old but he has been collecting and conserving plant genetic diversity since 1979 – six years before the Netherlands even had a national programme. His seed collection of 30,000 samples is probably the biggest private holding in all of Europe, and certainly surpasses Wageningen's.

Gus is critical of people who tell stories of what is going on at the grassroots level. There is not much grass in Utrecht and he hates to be called part of the 'informal' sector, but his work is an outstanding example of how people take the responsibility to care for diversity into their own hands. '*The danger with the stories,*' he says, '*is that the seeds will be lost. If people see others doing it, they will say "Look, there it is being done!" and won't bother to do anything themselves.*' There is obviously some truth to that. Yet if we don't tell stories, no one will see anything at all and the seeds may also be lost. We almost cannot afford not to take the chance.

Gus knows the staff and the scene at Wageningen but he is not too impressed. '*Oh, they are very nice people, but what they are conserving is not diversity. This Jaap Hardon, he has lots of lettuces, including so-called wild species. But have you ever seen them growing out? They're all the same! Look at my lettuces – they're all different! And those wild plants he says he's got are not wild at all. They have been domesticated to live in his genebank.*' Diversity is clearly in the eyes of the beholder.

Gus's living room is full of seeds. Only the chairs where we are sitting are not occupied by plants. Colanders filled with different, colourful beans are on the floor under the coffee table. '*These are landraces from Ethiopia. See how each of them is different? No two seeds are the same. I exchange lots of interesting materials with the genebank staff in Addis. They're doing wonderful work.*' On top of the coffee table there are heads of grains from last year's grow-out and all over the shelves and between the books, jars and jars of seeds. '*Do you want to see my genebank? It's a living genebank.*' This was a slight understatement. What Gus is running is a live-in genebank, starting with the living room.

We walk down a dark narrow hallway cluttered with old Dutch bicycles, boxes and muddy boots. '*This is the kitchen, but we can't eat here.*' His girlfriend smiles from across the room, but it's not clear whether the look on her face means this is terrific or she's had enough. For indeed, there is more food in the form of plantlets, dried vegetables, seeds, herbs and grains in their kitchen than could feed an army. Every shelf, table, countertop, cupboard and chair is littered with stocks of food plants in one form or another. But this is not for eating. It's for saving and growing and letting live. There is literally no room to put a sandwich down.

We go upstairs. '*This is the bedroom, but we can't sleep here.*' The bed is covered with cloths – not sheets and blankets – delicately holding tiny seeds drying slowly under the warm air blowing out from an electric heater, which is perched where a pillow should be propped. We climb another flight of twisted wooden stairs and reach what is starting to look like a very busy laboratory. One room is filled with plants that don't set true seed, growing under big lamps. Most of them are tropical plants from the Andes over to Tibet. '*Do you know Ulluco? It's what they call a "minor crop" but it's a major crop of the folk in the Andes. Actually, I'm specialised in minor crops. They're more interesting.*' Gus exchanges seeds with more than 600 'collaborators' in 100 countries around the planet. Some of them are official people from genebanks and research institutes, others are village people and friends of his who travel around and take seed to others on his behalf in exchange for something requested in return. African crops are his major gap right now.

The further we move up flights of stairs, the more boxes there are. Finally we reach the heart of the operation: the incoming and outgoing seeds. One room just holds the seeds that were grown out this year. They are carefully packaged in sealed envelopes to survive a few years in storage before hitting the soil again, and labelled with fine details for data processing. In the adjacent room, are the seeds that will be grown out in the next season. Despite the amazing quantities and sheer pandemonium of diversity all over the place, everything is meticulously organised. '*I have seven helpers growing out the seeds with me. One of them works full time at the computer, keeping all the information up to date.*'

It is quite a job. Each year, about 12,000 to 18,000 seed samples are regenerated in the outskirts of Utrecht. To maintain the integrity of the different varieties, Gus and his helpers grow the plants in little plots among the fields of small scale farmers in the region. In total, the area available to them amounts to 1.2 hectares. But his point is to save seeds so that they flourish in the field, not to grow them so that they can be stored in the house.

The only reason Gus is doing this is because he wants to. He is paid by the State to be permanently unemployed, by their definition, but he works seven days a week. To pay for some of the costs he also runs a non-profit seed company called Exclu-Seed. Each year, Gus and his associates offer a selected range of rare and unusual plant varieties to whoever is interested. Most of the clients are old people, who know plants, have time for them and remember what diversity used to be. Some of the seeds are very old cultivars, others are landraces and others yet are the Court of Eden's own creations. For example, this year the catalogue offers gardeners a chance to try a Nepalese lettuce landrace that is extremely variable. Gus asks his customers that if one particular plant in the heterogeneous batch is especially appealing, to please not eat it all, but let the plant go to seed and send the seeds back to the company so that they can multiply more seeds of that lettuce for other people to enjoy.

How so many tropical plants could survive in Utrecht leaves a lot of people perplexed. Gus's approach is straightforward: just don't interfere with them, let them do their own thing. His criteria for choosing which plants he takes on board are that they must be different, they must be natural and they must work for themselves, he is not going to work for them. But that doesn't mean he just sits back and whistles. If anything, Gus is a great observer and one of his keen interests is in crop development, crossing plants and creating new varieties. Nor is the point to be bundled up in Utrecht and prevented from living in his own house. The Court of Eden is trying to find the money to move to somewhere better suited to grow this diversity and show it to others. A 100 hectare plot of land in southeast Spain, where the microclimates are abundant, would be ideal. Would he mind if it were next to a Mitsubishi factory? '*All the better*!' Gus cried. '*We can do it with Mitsubishi*!'

### Breeding diversity biodynamically

Over in Mainleus, Germany, not far from Bayreuth and the old East German border, Martin Bossert is very grim. It's been hard going and it's just getting worse. For years now Martin has been working with the Association for the Promotion of Research and Education for Plant Breeding, an independent biodynamic research organisation set up in 1983. Otherwise known as the Pflanzenzuchtverein Wernstein, this group has taken on the vital but awesome challenge of breeding diversity back into German agriculture and helping scientific creativity thrive again outside the numbing grip of big business.

For Martin and his colleague Peter Raatsie, many of the problems associated with modern agriculture – the decline of food quality, of peoples' independence and of biological diversity – boils down to the seed. As farmers and gardeners give up seed saving and opt to purchase technical packages from an anonymous industry, they are giving up a lot more than just their seeds. *'Today, the knowledge of how to avoid a reduction in yield through adapted cultivation practices no longer exists or is becoming lost as well.'* Martin and Peter have been trying to reverse this trend, by breeding plants and developing farming systems that are sustainable and fertile, rather than simply high-yielding.

In their breeding work, carried out with farmers and horticulturalists in the region, they emphasise yield security, genetic variability, food quality, storage, taste and wholesomeness, and improved resistance. To do this, they have been collecting and conserving a broad range of genetic diversity in the form of old folk varieties from all over the region. They are currently maintaining several hundred varieties of more than one hundred species. As these crops were developed locally by farmers before chemicals were around, they are being tested as regional varieties for ecological agricultural production. They are also being conserved and improved for the future.

One important goal of their work is to revitalise seeds that have grown 'tired' through static and careless reproduction. For example, fundamental research on selecting rye through the so-called 'ear-bed' method of Martin Schmidt has allowed them to strengthen the vigour and fertility of other cereals and vegetables too. The ear-bed method involves sowing seeds in a row in the order they grow on the head of grain where the most mature are on the top and the youngest on the bottom. When you grow out the seeds respecting this order, the plants in the middle of the row will grow the tallest. Not only do yields increase, but these plants are also stronger and more resistant to stress than those at the edge of the row[5].

Martin and Peter have also been doing applied research to increase the nutritional value of food crops, the baking and storage qualities of grains and their health-enhancing properties. But all this intensive breeding and crop improvement depends on the availability of a good store of landraces and old cultivars. Their collection of varieties has been 40 years in the making and is composed of cereals, potatoes, beans and other vegetables, running into the hundreds. Every year, a fair portion of this diversity has to be grown out on a land area amounting to no more than one hectare. Last year, Martin sowed more than 25 different pulses alongside grains and vegetables to regenerate the seeds and keep the collection going.

But despite all this promising work, their efforts are constantly on the verge of being wiped out by the apathy of the authorities and the absence of financial resources to keep the operation alive. Everyone is pleased to admire the fine things they are doing, but few are pitching in to help. Last year when he came to Barcelona to join in a European network meeting of folk dedicated to genetic resources, Martin swore that he was about to bale out and just throw his whole collection of seeds into the fire. No one believed him; his commitment to keep fighting seemed too strong. But sustaining this work is impossible without resources and support. Would it help if he were allowed to sell his seeds and recoup some of the costs, despite German law prohibiting this? Martin is clear in rejecting this option. '*I am not interested in selling the seeds. I don't want to imitate the system that I am trying to find a way around.*'

### The destiny of Noah's Ark

A lot of folks who save seeds in Central Europe know Nancy Arrowsmith. Nancy is something of a minor monument on the scene. She has stubbornly lent her voice and muscle to help people in their struggle without ever hinting at giving up. Despite her frank and fierce complaints that she's sick and tired of the stories of how important genetic resources are and what a great thing grassroots conservation is, she buckles up and fights on.

Nancy lived in several countries, including Italy, the USA and Germany, before settling down in northeast Austria, not far from what was then the barbed wire of the Czechoslovakian border. Fascinated with the diversity of the landscapes and microclimates around her, she took on gardening 'with a vengeance,' as she puts it, and founded a magazine for fellow organic gardeners called *Kraut & Rüben*. This work, and the people around her, especially the elderly Austrian women who know something about saving their old varieties, got her going to conserve genetic diversity. For it took only a look around to see that there was a real problem. The seed business in Austria is not healthy. A full 95 per cent of the vegetable varieties come from foreign companies, which has the country in a state of great genetic dependence. As Nancy explains, the decline of Austrian plant breeding is not so much owing to takeovers and mergers, but to the wholesale wiping out of small businesses, which cannot keep up with competition from multinationals.

While this is already a problem, Nancy fears more for the imminent threats of tomorrow: Austria's integration into the European Community and entrance into the UPOV club of countries that provide Plant Breeders' Rights. Both of these changes are bound to take a heavy toll on whatever diversity farmers and gardeners are still enjoying in Austria, as can be seen in those countries that are already part of the systems. So one of Nancy's primary strategies in getting her seed work going has been systematically to collect the nonhybrid varieties still around but threatened by integration into the EC.

Today Nancy runs a network of seed savers in the German-speaking countries of Austria, Switzerland and Germany. She gave her organisation the biblical name Arche Noah or Noah's Ark from the idea of trying to load the boat with as much diversity as possible before the flood of erosion wipes it out. Today, there are more than 350 members in the network, collecting, maintaining and exchanging seeds through all sort of mechanisms: 'swap stands' at local markets, Arche Noah's publications or sympathetic health food stores. Nancy herself devotes 50 hours a week to her own seed saving of vegetables and keeping the organisation alive. Every year she publishes a catalogue of who is conserving what in the network and how to get hold of it. It offers hundreds of traditional varieties of cereals, vegetables, fruits, flowers, herbs and industrial crops. She also put together a listing of all nonhybrid seeds still available in Austria as of 1990, so that gardeners and farmers can save them before they are dropped from the market and disappear for good[6].

At the helm of Noah's Ark, she has a hard time smiling about it. *'We are not taken seriously by official institutions and have a long way to go before our organisation will be efficient enough to serve as a serious tool for the preservation of our plant heritage.'*[7] She herself has benevolently dumped plenty of her own private resources into the operation, while she desperately tries to get a grant from the government. The paperwork takes a lot of time and the results have not been encouraging. Until Noah's Ark can stand on its own feet, the work will remain a desperate battle against the demise of local diversity and people's legal liberty to save seed, even if it is patented. *'At the moment, our major role is that of a catalyst – to make farmers aware that they are losing their birthright, make consumers aware that they are losing valuable and delicious food plants, and make government officials and ecologists aware that there is a problem involved.'*[8]

Nancy is particularly vigilant about the situation in Eastern Europe, which is going through faster changes than her adopted home state of Austria. Over the years, she and her assistant Ursula Mitterbauer have gone collecting genetic resources in Czechoslovakia and Hungary, coming home with stocks of vegetables and fruits. They report, '*Parts of the Czechoslovakian countryside are so ravaged [by pollution and environmental damage] that not even potatoes will grow well. Mutations in leaf and in fruit forms are increasing in industrial areas.*'[9] The federal government's policy of industrial development repressed any option other than what it dictated as the only solution. The Czech seed supply has been the monopoly of the State and only officially accredited varieties are available to farmers and gardeners. In fact, usually only one variety per species was allowed to be grown in any given year.

Nancy also mourns what is happening in the former East Germany. Like other NGOs, she considers the genebank at Gatersleben to be one of the best in world, and praises its 'hands-on, practical approach to seed saving' practised by no other[10]. Yet its integration into West Germany's priorities will likely change all of that. Worse, in her view, is the demise of excellent grassroots conservation work apparently tolerated by the Communist regime and actively supported by the Gatersleben staff. Jürgen Reckin's Society for Ecological Plant Breeding and Soil Development stands out among the others. For years now, Jürgen and his team of eight dedicated scientists have been collecting, conserving and carrying out dynamic farming systems research with more than 300 varieties of grains, vegetables, amaranth, comfrey, legumes and forage crops. Nancy admires his work tremendously. He has developed wheat with good baking qualities and high protein content, potatoes resistant to frost, free-threshing spelt for small farmers, barleys that don't need chemical fertiliser and dozens of other local innovations to promote sustainable agriculture in East Germany. Yet the West German authorities have told Jürgen to shut down operations, as they consider this 'bad science'. As Nancy puts it, sadly, '*The excellent work of this group may be relegated into oblivion as quickly as the Berlin Wall.*'[11]

Nancy sees the rebuilding of local economies in the East as hinging upon the possibility of salvaging the old seeds that were at the heart of people's cultures and fight for independence. Much of this will have to come from the seed savers outside the region – refugees of the Ceauceauscu regime, Polish emigrants and others who fled from hardship with their seeds sewn into skirt linings and hidden in hat bands. Getting the local resources back into the tired and exploited villages is the kind of aid these regions need, not massive shipments of unadapted Western hybrids. Noah's Ark is more than willing to help transmit the seeds of the future back to these people. In so doing, Nancy and her friends would truly bring a legend to life.

## Fighting for options in the UK

'*I know it will happen again. I don't know what the next problem will be, I just know there is going to be one.*' Jeremy Cherfas is a biologist, gardener, seed saver and journalist based in Bristol. As his main source of income is as a freelance science writer, he is usually never sure of much, starting with where his next paycheque will come from so he can pay the mortgage and keep the roof over his head. But he is sure of one thing: that the genetic uniformity of our crops is setting us up for another major harvest loss that could make the Irish potato famine of the 19th century look like a minor event.

Jeremy is a member of the US-based Seed Savers Exchange and the UK's Henry Doubleday Research Association (HDRA). As his contribution to grassroots conservation Jeremy collects and maintains members of the onion family, with an emphasis on rare multiplier onions. He doesn't have time for more, although he would like to. Over the past couple of years, the little extra time he could squeeze away from writing articles has been invested in trying to revamp the HDRA's legendary vocation in sowing the seeds of diversity. Like any NGO, HDRA has had to make tough decisions about where to focus its emphasis and limited resources. Most of their work has been directed to developing a viable basis for organic gardening in the UK and overseas. But both the success and the sheer magnitude of this work has meant that attention has drifted away from genetic resources and the collection built up by HDRA's founder, Lawrence Hills. As Jeremy puts it, '*The HDRA's Heritage Seeds Programme and Heritage Seed Library had become a little like our seeds – slightly moribund.*'

It did not take Jeremy too long to convince today's leaders of the HDRA, Jackie and Alan Gear, that the genetic resources aspect of their programme needed a vital revamping. An independent review of the collection of 200 vegetables being conserved at Ryton Gardens near Coventry was carried out last year. The panel included staff from the Vegetable Genebank at Wellesbourne, and other scientists from the National Institute of Agricultural Botany. The review concluded that HDRA was indeed holding on to a heritage that was worth saving. But it had to be done fast.

The HDRA still doesn't have enough money to help Jeremy pay his mortgage by giving him a full-time job as their Head of Genetic Resources. The priority is to start growing out the seed collection and getting the newborn programme in action. While the seeds are revitalised in Coventry and backed up in cold storage at Wellesbourne, HDRA is trying get more people involved in their Seed Guardian scheme. Today there are about 40 Seed Guardians throughout the UK growing old varieties from the HDRA's Seed Library. They are responsible for producing enough seed for exchange within the network on a voluntary basis. Part of what prevents people getting involved in the programme is that many British gardeners, spoiled by instant products from commercial catalogues, have forgotten how to harvest and conserve seed from their crops. So HDRA is developing training courses and teaching materials of easy to learn techniques for what Jeremy calls 'saving backyard biodiversity'.

Another important part of the programme is raising public awareness about genetic diversity and why it is vital to use and preserve our rich gardening heritage. A display of illegal varieties at this year's Chelsea Flower Show certainly did that! Not only did it attract almost 500 new members for the Heritage Seed Programme, it also attracted a bronze medal from the stuffy Royal Horticultural Society. '*At last, people are beginning to take some notice*,' says Jeremy.

To HDRA and other UK organisations working to promote sustainable agriculture, an important feature of the old varieties is that even if they don't yield as much as fancy hybrids and other modern strains, they don't demand the external inputs that are poisoning Britain's environment, water and food supply and costing farmers an arm and a leg. If those concerns don't stir British citizens, their shopping basket might. '*Consumers are being ripped off.*' Jeremy is emphatic about this point. '*Taste, if it figures at all, has generally been low on the list of priorities in the development of modern varieties. Shoppers are beginning to resent that.*' These wider costs of today's food production system are only slowly starting to be calculated and felt.

But people in Britain are mostly moved by the genetic uniformity argument, and probably for a good reason. The UK is one country where NGOs have hit hardest on their government to take a more responsible role towards managing the resource base of agriculture. And the UK is one country where the government has not done very much. Wellesbourne is one example. But what about Brogdale? Great Britain's – and probably the world's – largest collection of fruit trees nearly died a few years ago because the government could not care less. Through private efforts, involving the HDRA's royal patron Prince Charles, the collection was saved from extinction and is now run as the Brogdale Horticultural Trust. Had no one batted an eye when the government sold off the UK's historic Plant Breeding Institute to Unilever, their genetic resources collection, long built up as a public heritage, would have been sold off with it. And only now is the government starting to contemplate something in the range of a national policy on genetic resources. By all accounts, the British have narrowly avoided losses as their administrators have persisted in believing that if the sacrosanct market doesn't value the country's genetic heritage it should be scrapped.

But HDRA is mostly worried about the future of Britain's food security. Saving seeds is not just for the pleasure of growing something different in your garden. NGOs and individuals have a major role to play in decentralising the conservation effort and multiplying what is in effect an insurance premium against crop wipeout. As Alan Gear puts it, '*The history of agriculture is littered with epidemics of disease and outbreaks of pest; in almost every case, salvation was found either in an old variety or in a wild relative of the crop.*'[12] To contribute to this effort, HDRA has just published a new version of *The Vegetable Finder*. A catalogue of catalogues, it lists all vegetable varieties legally available in the UK today: 1,973 open-pollinated types and 829 hybrids. This is not quite the abundant and secure offering of diversity it seems. Nearly 60 per cent – more than 1,000 – of the non-hybrid vegetables are being maintained by one solitary supplier and are marked with a special symbol.

Of course, seed-saving in the UK would be a lot more efficient if people could sell heirloom varieties, but this is restricted by the law, as in many other Western European countries. The standards for uniformity set a high barrier to enter the seed market and effectively keep folk varieties off the shelf. Even if a scientifically competent organisation like HDRA went into plant breeding, it would need considerable funds to compete with the top companies. It costs £1,800 these days to register a variety on the National List and another £400 each year to keep it there, whether it sells one hundred packets or one hundred thousand. So an NGO like HDRA doesn't – and can't – 'sell' seeds. '*I give you the seeds, and you give me a donation,*' Jeremy explains. '*We don't like loopholes, but that's the way it has to be.*' Until the regulations are changed, the right to compete on the seed market will be a right reserved for the already rich.

Meanwhile, Jeremy and other British groups are set to continue the fight to raise awareness, bring the grassroots actors closer together and create a new demand for diversity. '*Not in a simple-minded nostalgia of "Gee, weren't the apples better when we were kids,"* ' he stresses. '*That's not the point. But we have to get everyone to realise ultimately that the diversity we are trying to preserve is going to feed them in the future.*'

## SAVING THE SEED

### Recovering the future of Tuscany

Giovanni Cerretelli is deeply worried about where farming is going in Italy. Not just the pesticide problem and people leaving the land. He is mostly concerned about the loss of local varieties and with them the heart and culture of the people who nurtured them as a bridge to tomorrow. In a race against the loss of the future, he has spent the past couple of years visiting old farmers and gardeners in Tuscany, talking to them about the seeds their families grew, the history of how and why different varieties were developed and handed down, what they were valued for and how they were grown. The past is rich, but the future is uncertain.

'*We can collect the germplasm, but unless young people learn how to save seeds again and keep the links intact, this diversity will not thrive.*' Giovanni is an agronomist and wants to help farmers develop more sustainable production systems. Together with Francesca Castioni and a few other colleagues, he set up a cooperative in Florence called Il Bigallo Verde, with the aim of offering to local farmers services, advice and training on biological agriculture. The value of traditional varieties became evident to him. Generally well adapted to local conditions, they could provide resistance, nutritional value, taste, self reliance and a stability of yield under low input practices that the modern varieties can't match.

In 1986, Bigallo Verde started a project to rescue old crop varieties in Tuscany with the support of the regional government and the Agricultural University of Florence. Before collecting, a lot of research went into figuring out where to go and what to look for. This meant talking to local farmers to get a first-hand picture of the map of the region's agricultural history. Once the field trips got underway, it became clear that while a lot of diversity had been lost, especially in areas of intensive industrialised farming, there was still a range of traditional cultivars being grown, especially among small farmers and the elderly. To date, more than 200 samples of crop plants have been collected, mostly local vegetables, cereals, pulses and forage crops.

The collecting work opened Giovanni's eyes to the eminently social and human dimension of seeds and the critical lack of a good conservation system in the region – one in which farmers are directly involved. '*On many occasions, we were able to become aware of the extent to which the cultivation of local plants is tied to a precise local culture on its way to extinction, or, unfortunately at times, recovered only in its more aesthetic forms.*'[13] Most of the material collected came from elderly small-scale farmers who have maintained their rural traditions and for whom reproducing their own seed was one of the most fundamental

**110**

activities on the farm. But as these people are dying out, someone has to safeguard their seeds for them.

Culturally, politically and technically, Italy's national genebank in Bari is too far away. Tuscany needs a regional approach to managing its genetic resources or it won't work. '*The local varieties collected have to continue to circulate as the wealth of the farmers.*'[14] If the seeds are cut off from the people, they will lose their real value as a local heritage. What sense and benefits will Tuscan farmers derive by shipping their seeds to a central storage unit down south? Giovanni says it again and again: the imperative is not conservation as such, but utilisation, putting diversity to work in local economies.

Giovanni and his colleagues from the official sector are firm about moving forward. Collecting must continue but conservation begins with what has already been salvaged. The first task is to multiply the seeds so that there is more to work with. Then the seeds have to be safely preserved for the future. Tuscany is set on creating its own regional genebank but only in cooperation with farmers. While cold storage is vital, they feel it is just as vital to provide farmers with the proper incentives and opportunities to keep the local varieties alive by growing them within sustainable production systems. Given the circumstances today, this will mean identifying the varieties with good forms of resistance and integrating them into low-energy production systems that don't need pesticides and can improve the quality of food and the environment.

The task ahead is tremendous and Giovanni can't count all the hurdles to overcome. Probably the biggest and most important to him is getting this diversity back into the farms and the villages so that people can relate to it again. For that to happen, people will need to learn how to save, reproduce and select seeds so that they can really work again with plants and use the possibilities offered by local cultivars for a more ecological and self-reliable approach to producing food. But at the same time, consumers will have to learn to demand this kind of diversity in their quest for higher quality products and a cleaner environment. The bottom line is clear: we can't move into the future if we are not armed with the past.

## *A full-time conservation group in Switzerland* [15]

Switzerland is one of the few European countries where the national genebank has actually put some of the old varieties it collected from farmers back into production, mainly rustic mountain cereals donated to biological farming organisations. But relations between the official and non-official sectors are not always so harmonious and trusting. In the late 1970s, some sceptical people did not believe the government's claim that there was not much more to do to conserve the old breeds of Swiss farm animals; what was gone was gone, it was said. The sceptics went out and scoured valley after valley, stable after stable identifying what was really left. They found many breeds that were said to be extinct. Somehow, the State had not been very efficient!

In early 1980, these diversity-hunters founded a private non-governmental organisation and named it Pro Specie Rara (PSR). The idea was to develop an independent and participatory approach to maintaining the genetic diversity of Swiss plants and animals. Rather than acting as a club or a network, PSR functions as a kind of trust fund for endangered animals. Its finances comes from its own shareholders, patronage and grants. With its working capital, PSR buys the last individuals of a breed and 'rents' them out free of charge to interested farmers. The farmer has full use of the animals while PSR maintains the right to buy the offspring and enlarge the herd. PSR manages the herdbook and directs mating strategies. When the breed is out of danger of extinction, the foundation relinquishes its rights over the animals and, as PSR staffer Hans-Peter Grünenfelder puts it, 'a free market takes place'. The idea of this controlled procedure is to spread the animals out in small and decentralised breeding groups to avert any risks and keep the highest number of males, to guarantee a wide genetic base.

Much of PSR's success and experience has been with animals: cattle, sheep, goats, pigs and also fowl, such as chickens and geese. They are really best known for this original and popular work. For a few years, however, they have also been working with plants, collecting and multiplying old varieties through a parallel network of participating gardeners and horticulturalists. Their priorities are limited to crops adapted to high altitudes and the rigours of Swiss mountain climates. Rustic potato cultivars, such as the Eight-Week Potato and old farmers' varieties of legume crops and cereals have been collected and are available for growing.

Pro Specie Rara has enjoyed a lot of success at home. Rather than conserving species in one special place so they don't die out, they offer people a chance to get involved directly, either by adopting a breed financially, housing some animals or growing out traditional varieties. Today nearly 400 Swiss farmers are involved in their animal rescue operations, while 250 fruit and vegetable growers maintain the plants they have collected. Amazingly, this organisation has survived and carried out all its work without any funding from the government. A rare feat indeed.

PSR is growing – and eastward bound. They are not becoming another Swiss multinational, but because of their location in the centre of the 'new' Europe, it was impossible for them to ignore what was taking place in nearby East European countries. Their fears that economic restructuring of the former communist regimes would bring about the rapid loss of traditional animal breeds, fruit stocks and crops – not 'profitable' enough for the future market economy – have all too quickly materialised. In 1989, PSR sent staff into Czechoslovakia to search out the indigenous breeds and found that the dramatic end to the lives of many had begun. Many a rare animal finally tracked down through local farmers was found hanging up on a butcher's hook. In one desperate move, they tried to export some specimens of the famous wooly-backed Mangalizza pigs into Switzerland for safety and reproduction. The pigs were held at the border for quarantine, and it turned out that they were infected with a virus. The pigs sat there for a year, while PSR nervously put up the money, until it was known whether the offspring were healthy.

The agricultural genetic wipeout in the East is so serious and violent that PSR has set up an office in Prague to instigate and coordinate emergency conservation projects – with just the money they can spare from their Swiss activities. Another office is being established in the former Yugoslavia. Together with other grassroots conservation organisations in Central Europe they are trying to set up an umbrella Euro-Fund or Euro-Association that will link up animal and plant heritage groups throughout the region to capitalise jointly on the little available funding and increase cooperative activities. With the clock ticking so fast, equally rapid action to salvage the backyard breeds of generations of private farmers and gardeners in the East is urgent. The pleas for help coming from the official sector may fall on deaf ears in the West. Let us hope that concerted NGO action can make up for this and result in something effective for the future.

## Quality and competence at Le Biau Germe

Sylvia Schmid is a petite women with silvery hair and a gentle voice. Neither an ageing hippie nor a newborn ecologist, Sylvia abounds with common sense and simplicity. When she talks about the old varieties of tomatoes and peaches that farmers and gardeners cultivated in France decades ago, she seems mesmerised by their qualities and defects, the

**113**

panorama of different breeds that suited different climates and uses, and the opportunities they offer to keep on experimenting and developing new types.

We first crossed paths with Sylvia in the early 1980s when she decided to go into the seed business. It wasn't the typical seed business, however. Sylvia wanted to cater to a commonsense clientele of people who could appreciate regionally adapted varieties that were grown without chemicals. She wanted to rescue the best of France's wealth in local varieties from oblivion – but without getting nostalgic or folklorish about it. From the moment she started, the law was against her. With her starting batch of traditional varieties, she went into small scale production and began announcing that the old seeds were back on sale and would work wonderfully on organic farms. She couldn't afford to advertise in any broad fashion like the mainstream merchants of grain. But she did manage to slip her message through the local press and into biological farming circles.

Thus her fight of common sense against reality began. The authorities threatened that what she was doing was illegal. Her varieties were not registered on France's national list of seeds that could be legally sold. But how could she possibly comply with the regulation? The law held that varieties had to be unique, uniform and stable, which no landrace or old farmer's variety possibly could. And she could not afford to try to register anything, even if it were possible. She was warned to shut down operations or risk legal action.

It was then that, shocked by disbelief, Sylvia contacted us for confirmation that it was true that she was doing something unlawful and for advice on what to do. She could not believe that in a democratic country such as France it was illegal to pursue another type of agricultural development than the one farmers were coerced into by the chemical industry. Nor could she believe that the genetic heritage painstakingly developed by farmers and gardeners and handed down over generations was barred from survival by government decree and had to be relegated to underground channels and misfit adventurers just to stay alive.

We did not have to argue anything in return, we only offered our support if any of the threats against her integrity materialised. Yes she was breaking the law, but if that was the only way to demonstrate the foolishness of the law, it was up to her to take the chance. Sylvia stuck with her belief in the value of the old seeds and the interest they offered for the development of sustainable agriculture and in the ten years since her perilous start, the enterprise has bloomed into one of the most well-respected and appealing biological seed companies in France.

**114**

The Biau Germe is implanted in southwest France, where the soils and climate are not too bad for seed production. The operation is run by Sylvia, her brother, Rene, and his wife, Annie, now assisted by one other couple, Pascal and Veronique Naudin. Together, they have four hectares of land for seed production, spread out to avoid cross pollination. Biau Germe has two principal objectives. First, to produce seeds whose genetic potential has not been altered by chemicals and can therefore continue to maintain and develop their natural vigour. Secondly, to participate in the management of our genetic heritage by producing seeds of old varieties, with a particular emphasis on those cultivated before the First World War.

Sylvia and her gang work hard to produce the finest quality seed for amateurs and gardeners. They carry out very strict germination controls to deliver a potent product and take great care in adjusting production to changing demands. For example, oriental vegetables are becoming popular now in many countries of Western Europe: Chinese cabbages and greens, edible chrysanthemums, and so on. The Biau Germe tests them out for truly dependable results under small farm conditions in temperate climates and cautiously advises their clients on how best they grow. When there is time, they also do some breeding and selection to improve crops and develop them further. But their favourites are the old time classics that bring farming and gardening down to its real nature: a true art in juggling the complex factors that work on and off each other in a diversified environment. For example, they take pride in keeping available the tall Red Wheat of Bordeaux, a very old and rustic landrace that is well adapted to low-input farming practices, returns a lot of straw to the soil and produces an exceptionally nutritious grain without chemicals. They also offer well-prepared and well-tested varietal mixtures of a number of horticultural and ornamental crops – something unknown to the mainstream seed market geared towards uniformity!

Despite her success, Sylvia is still in limbo with the law. Due to pressure from grassroots organisations, France did create a special parallel registration system for old fruit varieties in the mid-1980s – the only European country to do so, but also the only European country with any registration requirement for fruits. The standards are less rigorous and the fees lower. But what about the rest? Sylvia has been negotiating with other organic seed producers to form a trade union to defend their rights to exist on the market. But in the meantime, the French authorities are starting to realise that the system doesn't make sense. If there is a demand for traditional varieties and people are willing to produce them on a commercial scale, why shouldn't they be allowed to do business? Her sheer obstinacy may win Sylvia the satisfaction of seeing the laws rewritten to recognise the value of our genetic heritage. And of the common sense behind people's drive to work with diversity and let it thrive, for our own pleasure and that of generations to come.

## Seed saving in Sweden

SESAM is a small non-profit organisation in Sweden, working to maintain a pool of local crop varieties well adapted to the Nordic climates. With nearly two hundred members participating in the network, SESAM is reviving and revitalising the art of cultivating seeds for the future.

The main activity of the organisation is teaching people how to grow and save seed crops of local varieties in the different climates of Sweden. When a member of the group has proven that he or she has mastered the art of managing a certain species, that person is commissioned to grow out an old variety for the benefit of the others. One senior member is responsible for overseeing training and management of the collection for each crop group: peas, beans, carrots and so forth. A minimum number of plants per variety have to be regularly grown out to ensure long-term maintenance and availability of seeds. At the same time, part of the overall collection is backed-up in cold storage compartments as a safety measure.

SESAM Chairperson Thomas Levander explains the limits of this approach. '*All work within the association is done on a voluntary basis and in our spare time. We are strictly amateurs at the grassroots level. So far we have no sponsors or any financial support for our work.*' On the positive side, Thomas is certain that this kind of work is an invaluable contribution to keeping alive well-adapted varieties that are suited to the region. If everyone just turned their backs on genetic erosion and let the country's crop heritage disappear, how would Swedish farming survive in the future?

Take the potato. Over the years, SESAM has developed a broad collection of old potato landraces that have long worked well in Sweden's diverse agro-ecosystems. However, most of them are now suffering from virus plagues and reduced vitality. Thomas and his colleagues managed to raise some money to pay a research institute to do meristem culture of their infected stock and start cleaning up this heritage collection so that new clones will ensure its survival. In the meantime, they are figuring out how to develop a virus-free environment to be able to continue growing these folk varieties that are well-appreciated and worth saving.

The SESAM network has proved to itself that there is a job to do and its membership is qualified to do it. They would even like to grow and link up with similar groups engaged in seed saving of Nordic cultivars in Finland and Denmark. The problem is the lack of resources and time to further the research. The starting basis is there, but developing adequate techniques for different species in different zones takes quite some effort. And though they would like and need to, there is simply no time to investigate characteristics like pest resistance, cropping systems and other features that would help reinstate farmers' varieties into today's production systems. Even describing the old cultivars can be a headache.

Until there are resources available to give this work deeper foundations, the first priority is to link up with other organisations and learn from each other. SESAM's members have taught themselves a lot and learned how to conserve genetic resources at the farmer level the hard way. They are really keen to share their experiences with other groups and build on their achievements in a solid and sustainable manner.

## *Managing the genetic heritage of Provence*

Cooperation between the formal and informal sectors is not only necessary, it is also possible. This, at least, is the lesson to be learned from what is probably Europe's only adventure in mounting a fully fledged regional genetic heritage programme that involves a wide range of actors in an incredibly full spectrum of activities.

PAGE PACA is the name of the initiative born in 1983 and hopefully here to stay and grow. PAGE stands for 'PAtrimoine GEnétique' (or Genetic Heritage) and PACA for Provence-Alpes-Cotes d'Azur which is the name of the region in the southeast of France, comprised of six administrative departments and covering nearly 31,500 square kilometres of extremely diverse ecosystems. The climate is Mediterranean but the topography ranges from the sandy shores of St Tropez to the upper Alps, passing through plains and lower mountain chains, prairies, orchards and small river valleys.

The genetic and cultural diversity of the area is rich but underexploited and ill-preserved. Recognising this, a whole range of activities were springing up from different circles to conserve and utilise the resources of the region: national parks, organic farming organisations, schools, research institutes and NGOs. Agriculture was going through rapid transformations. For example, the region has become specialised in fruit production and early vegetables, exported throughout the country. But the local orchards were ripped up and re-planted with varieties from California. Honey production has also been an old vocation of the region and earned farmers, gardeners and private individuals a bit of extra income that never hurt. Yet the indigenous Black Bee of Provence, so well adapted to the climate and flowers of the zone, was being sacrificed to the spread of imported hybrid races that yielded well but did not really integrate into the ecosystem.

People from all corners of the region were getting concerned about the decline of their heritage in the face of easy solutions that might not be sustainable. The problem was not just agricultural, nor just environmental, but really had to do with valuing and utilising the wealth of traditional knowledge long generated by centuries of working with local resources. Rather than work in a fragmented way, the different actors sat down and forged a plan for cooperation that won the support and encouragement of their regional government, as well as from Paris' Ministry of the Environment.

PAGE PACA brings together more than thirty agencies, from grassroots NGOs and biological farming organisations to the State's agronomic research institute, INRA, and national parks. Their main goal is not only to conserve but also to foment sustainable economic development in the region by harnessing local knowledge and resources. As an umbrella organisation for the multiple partners, PAGE PACA lends logistical support to local initiatives or else designs new programmes at the regional level which different members will take up and carry out.

In the first years of its work, the programme has focused on a vast range of species, activities and industries. As fruits are a major cash crop of the region, PAGE PACA has inventoried the traditional fruits of the zone, collected what could still be found and is preserving and studying the old types for reintegration into the economy. For example, rare and valuable varieties such as the Blood Peach of Manosque, with its ruby red flesh, or the Snow Peach, which bears unusual white flowers, have been recovered from near extinction against the onslaught of modern hybrids. Local figs, almonds, plums and cherries have followed the same path. Many have found their way into the orchard being set up at La Thomassine, PAGE PACA's demonstration and research farm, near the village of Manosque. Doubles of many materials are backed up at the National Botanical Garden run by Louis Olivier on the island of Porquerolles.

Many of these cultivars are exceptionally resistant to diseases and pests and provide succulent fruit. But of course they lack the hard skins that would make them transportable over long distances – an end for which they were not developed by earlier farming families. One answer to this problem is to develop processed goods based on these and other unique local fruits: jams, juices, syrups and pastes. But that demands setting up relations with local industrialists willing to help find novel ways of processing the raw materials into adapted products. Another is to encourage direct local consumption of the region's heritage through schools, markets and restaurants.

Provence has also long been a grazing land of goats and sheep that fed superbly on leguminous forages like sainfoin. As this grass is well adapted to the climates and soils, PAGE PACA has collected old ecotypes and is experimenting with farmers on developing its production once again. It can be intercropped with cereals and used as a green manure or cut and fed to sheep. Other experiments have been carried out with local breeds of clover, alfalfa and vetches, which are compared with modern commercial varieties in on-farm trials. The difference is generally the same: local ecotypes are less demanding and better adapted to the complexities of the Provençal region. The drawback is that there is no source of seed nor distribution system for the indigenous varieties.

In the area of vegetables, aromatic and medicinal plants, a lot of collecting has saved many old varieties from dying out. The same goes for animal breeds, honey flowers and indigenous bees. But once the problem of setting up inventories, collecting materials and getting them into active maintenance is resolved, the real challenge is utilising them in viable economic circuits. This is not just a problem of supply but also of demand. Raising public awareness about the value and utility of local genetic resources has been a major activity of PAGE PACA. Campaigns with slogans like 'Our Genetic Heritage is Everyone's Business' or 'Resources of the Future, Jobs for Tomorrow' have been launched to teach the public and help them understand that responsibility for managing local diversity has to be collective, not just dependent on the State or anyone else.

But perhaps most of all, the greatest success of the programme thus far has been in bringing very different actors together to work towards a common goal in a concrete setting. Philippe Barret, NGO member of the Board of PAGE PACA, is proud of this fact and cherishes the good relations he has with members from INRA and the formal conservation circles. '*We have different perceptions and different priorities, but we have learned to work together and respect our differences.*' If diversity is to thrive, it can only really do so in such an environment.

# 5: Diversifying the future

## Forging new policies

The challenge of developing a suitable policy agenda for effective and deep-rooted action in the way we manage the plant genetic resource base of our economies is a tremendous one. We desperately need an umbrella framework, a democratically elaborated action plan that grasps society's rationale for preserving and using biological diversity. Right now, there is a wide range of multiple policies and regulations in operation that deeply affect genetic resources management. Several of them contradict each other. Farm policies push farmers to demand a very low level of diversity and depend instead on external, productivity-pumping technologies. Seed marketing schemes and intellectual property rights laws crown this by pushing research and development toward high uniformity and low innovation. Against this, conservation efforts are almost totally separated from the market and production sphere. Environmental protection programmes throughout Europe provide government money to run nature reserves and parks, to preserve ecosystems and let them evolve without economic intervention. Other budgets go into preserving seeds in genebanks, from a mixture of research and heritage preservation logics.

The incoherence is manifest, but the interests of conservation and production are not irreconcilable. On the contrary, they are inseparable. Unfortunately they have been violently divorced for the past few decades with the aim of promoting short-term industrial development at the expense of long-term agricultural resource management. These broken stitches will have to be mended and the policy fabric reformed.

If we are to conserve and effectively utilise the rich opportunities that plant genetic diversity offers to us, then we need a policy framework to guide more responsible action. Policy issues are hard to wrestle with because of the different and often conflicting interests at stake. But they are critical to design and implement as a rationale for action.

**120**

There are four general policy areas that affect plant genetic resources management in Europe. One of them concerns environmental policy. In and of itself, this area has received a lot of attention over the past few years and nature conservation programmes are abundant. They are important and they need strengthening, but the point is that they are at least moving in an active direction. Three other fields are in drastic shape and need major revisions if we are to take plant genetic resources and sustainability at all seriously. They concern agricultural policy, the legal frameworks and the research agenda. This trinity has a heavy influence on the utilisation of our genetic heritage. They are intrinsically tied to the question: what kind of development do we want in Europe?

## CAP: Conservation or production?

What to do with the European Community's Common Agricultural Policy (CAP) has probably been one of the most hotly debated issues in Europe over the past decade. It has come under attack from farmers, environmentalists, industrialists and Third World groups alike. The essence of the CAP is basically a system of guaranteed farm prices for specific products, way above those at world market levels, combined with various measures to block the entry of cheaper products from outside the Community. In the public eye, the CAP is often associated with surplus production and escalating costs. In 1991, the EC spent 33 billion ECU (some US$ 45 billion), or 60 per cent of its entire budget, on CAP alone. But the bulk of this money does not go to the farmers. A full two-thirds of it is devoted to non-productive activities such as stockpiling and destruction of the surpluses, or getting rid of them on the world market through export subsidies.

In recent years, EC governments and Eurocrats alike have been growing more and more alarmed about this policy-induced nightmare: an ever-rising bill for an agriculture that employs an ever-shrinking minority of Europeans. But the real pressure to overhaul the current CAP comes from the GATT negotiators and foreign countries such as the USA, which see the EC price and export subsidies, combined with protectionist measures to stop cheap agricultural products from entering the EC market, as unfair competition for their own farmers.

The heart of the now agreed upon CAP reform is a dramatic 30 per cent cut in prices paid to cereal farmers until 1994, topped off by a 15 per cent reduction in beef prices and a 5 per cent lowering of butter prices, among others. These cuts are designed to move EC farm output towards world market price levels and progressively eliminate current subsidies. The European Commission argues that high prices paid to EC farmers in the past have stimulated dangerously intensive forms of agriculture together with the encumbrance of surplus production and environmental pollution. The new price reductions will, according to the Commission, help arrest further intensification of agriculture and thus alleviate the escalating damage to the environment.

All this sounds wonderful, but in reality things might be quite different. Farmers in the EC have indeed benefited from guaranteed prices above world market levels. But those prices paid to farmers have been progressively lowered over the years while more and more money is devoted to export subsidies. By increasing export subsidies, the EC ends up dumping its produce on the world market, which itself leads to lower prices to compete with. Thus the vicious circle gets worse and worse.

Contrary to the Commission's projections, farm price reductions in the EC have always lead to greater intensification and more surplus production. Between 1963 and 1983, EC cereal prices were reduced by 45 per cent, and since then by another 30 per cent. During this period, agricultural production increased and surpluses built up. Obviously, if farmers are faced with lower prices they either go out of business or they increase production, depending on whether they can make further investments or not. The EC farming community has declined 35 per cent over the past 15 years, while ever increasing production has become concentrated among fewer and fewer farms. Today, 60 per cent of the EC's grains are produced by only 6 per cent of the Community's cereal farmers, 75 per cent of the milk comes from 25 per cent of the dairy farms, and 80 per cent of the pigs are raised by 10 per cent of the pork producers. Slashing prices yet again under the new CAP regime is more than likely to step up this process: further concentration of production on fewer farms, which will have to drastically intensify their production methods in order to keep up.

### Compensation . . . for whom?

The other side of the CAP reform coin is compensation. The policy-makers recognise that the newly imposed price levels are below the production costs of three-quarters of Europe's farmers, who will have to retire or find another job if nothing else is done. Only a quarter of Europe's largest farmers would be able to keep up with the lower prices if they manage to increase output and lower their costs. So a system of compensation payments is being set up according to the number of hectares each farmer was planting, in the case of cereals for example, and the average yield in each region, before the CAP reform. Thus, if you are a farmer in a high yield region and you have done your best to increase EC surplus production over the past years, you are likely to get most of the compensation. However, if you happen to be a farmer in a disadvantaged part of Europe that tends to provide low yields and harbour small farming production systems, you'll end up getting the smallest part of the cake and a compensation that keeps you in the same trouble as you were in before.

In modelling the reform, one '*mea culpa*' of the EC Commission was that, up until now, the bulk of the price subsidies ended up with the minority of well-off farmers. However, with the new compensation system linked to yield and acreage, the same is likely to happen. It is calculated that 80 per cent of the compensation will end up in the hands of 20 per cent of Europe's farmers. The end result is that the 20 per cent better-off farms in the EC will, on the one hand, react to lowered prices by further intensifying their production, and on the other hand, catch most of the compensation from Brussels.

Obviously, an important question for farmers is: how long will the compensation last? And for the national governments: how much will it cost? Nobody really knows. Apart from the costs of the compensation system itself, a huge bureaucracy will have to be put in place to monitor who has the right to what compensation. In one German *land*, Bavaria, it is estimated that over 200 extra staff are needed to do the counting. Officials from the EC Commission swear that the compensations will be paid until the end of time. But farmers rightly remain sceptical. As one observer stated to the press, '*The farmers know that they are being paid to do nothing. That is a very vulnerable position to be in.*' The first attack against the compensation package might already come this year from the UK, whose turn at the rotating six-month EC presidency began in July 1992 with the firm intention to lower EC expenditure on just about everything. It might very well be that the compensation system merely serves as a short-term bait on paper to get the larger farmers' unions to accept the reform package and close the discussion.

### Set aside . . . for what?

One major condition for the large farms to receive the compensation is that they have to set aside at least 15 per cent of their arable land, which means not using it for food production. This measure is intended to ensure that

EC farm surpluses are once and for all cut down. Many doubt whether it will really work to that effect, though. The set aside scheme is basically imported from the United States – where it has proved *not* to work. Despite 20 years of its application in the US, the system backfired: surplus production has increased continuously there, while whole regions have been losing their farmers.

The CAP set aside scheme is also often presented as a neat way to reduce production and recover soil productivity by taking the pressure off part of Europe's arable land. This is simply not true. 'Setting aside' land in the new policy is not defined as leaving it alone to recover from intensive practices: heavy machines, toxic pesticides, chemical fertilisers, massive irrigation and draining. It means, rather, that farmers are not allowed to grow food *per se* on it. This is where Europe's biomass advocates come in. Potatoes, colza, cereals and all sorts of other crops can be grown on the set aside land if they are used for non-food purposes such as making bioethanol, biocarburants, starch and other components for industrial use. Piles of studies are financed by the EC Commission and special subsidy programmes go to industry to make it technically feasible to use the set aside land more intensively than ever by producing raw materials for a newly emerging biomass industry. As long as you don't grow 'food' on the set aside land, you are free to do what you want with it. There is no limit on the amount of chemical fertiliser, herbicides or pesticides you can use on this land. Rather than reduce production, the set-aside rule will, again, intensify it.

If you are a large 'competitive' farmer and are not interested in the biomass business, there is an easy way around the set aside scheme. The set aside quotas are tradeable with other farmers. So farmers with poor soils might obtain and accumulate set aside parts from large farmers working on the best soils who then have their hands free to grow whatever surplus they want. As there are no rules about with whom you can trade your set aside land, we might end up with a situation in which the better-off farmers in northern France, UK and Denmark continue to produce Europe's food surplus, while entire regions in Greece, Spain and Portugal are officially 'set aside'.

### Europe going green?

All in all, the reform will push European agriculture further into the split that was ripped open with the launching of the first CAP decades ago: 'real' intensive and large farms provide the bulk of Europe's agricultural output, while the 'unproductive' smaller farms can't keep up. To a large extent that split is geographical. The EC Commission divides Europe into 'advantaged' and 'disadvantaged' regions. Currently, the 'real' crop farming is done by large holdings concentrated in northern France, and parts of England and Denmark, while the intensive animal production takes place in the Netherlands, parts of Belgium, northern Germany and northern Italy. These farms roughly account for 25 per cent of the Community's agricultural land, while the remaining 75 per cent is dismissed as lacking economic efficiency.

By lowering prices and channelling the bulk of compensation payments to the already 'advantaged' regions and farms, this split will be further enhanced. With the current CAP reform there is simply no agricultural future for 75 per cent of the Community's farmers. For some countries, such as Spain, Portugal and Greece, this means that there is no future for agriculture at all, as virtually all of their farmers fall into this 'disadvantaged' group. But also in the better-off countries, many farmers will not survive the onslaught. In trying to figure out the future of their pesticide sales, the German agro-industry already reckons that only 80,000 of Germany's 400,000 farmers will be in business by the year 2002. The industry remains optimistic, though, as they expect that those fewer farmers will actually increase their use of chemicals to intensify operations.

The masterminds behind the CAP reform figured that they had to do something for the losers, and came up with a series of 'accompanying measures'. With 75 per cent of Europe's farmers not needed any more for production purposes, the policy-makers decided to use some of the arguments of conservation groups by saying that the time has now come to recognise that farmers have an important role in the protection of the rural environment and management of landscapes, and that they should be recompensed accordingly. The move is clever in several respects. It allows the CAP reformers to present their package as 'socially just' and 'environmentally friendly', as for the first time these considerations are explicitly taken into account. Proudly presented as the 'Agri-Environmental Action Programme', this new part of CAP offers subsidies to farmers if they start growing organically without chemicals or stop draining, irrigation and ploughing up meadows. You can also get money if you stick to rare breeds or local crop varieties in danger of extinction.

But small farmers will have to hurry, if they want to pocket any of the ECUs earmarked for 'environmental services'. The budget is extremely limited: 400 million ECU (some US$ 540 million) in the first year, up to 900 million (or US$ 1.2 billion) in the fifth year. Beyond then, no further guarantees. This is merely 1 to 2 per cent of what Brussels spends right now on its agricultural policies! And it is meant for three-quarters of the Community's farmers, who otherwise have no future at all!

## Delinking agriculture and environment

Despite the enthusiastic reactions from EC bureaucrats, hard-nosed economists and free-traders worldwide, the new CAP reform is directing Europe's agriculture straight towards a profound disaster. Basically the reform amounts to a violent separation of a 'productive' and 'competitive' minority that produces the bulk of Europe's food and raw materials for industry, and a written-off majority that gets paid to do some environmentally-friendly freewheeling or just go out of business.

With respect to genetic resources management and the vulnerability of our uniform crops and livestock, the reform could not be more sinister. Forced to increase productivity further, the competitive minority will be more demanding of and reliant upon ever fewer varieties and animal breeds to be able to attain the maximum results. Already, the most productive European farmers plant no more than one or two of the highest yielding crop varieties, each of them genetically uniform. This trend will unfortunately only be reinforced by the new CAP. Europe's agro-ecosystems will be further standardised and concentrated in fewer areas that allow for even fewer crop varieties to be sown on larger acreages. With the new CAP we are definitely heading towards a European agriculture based on the same wheat from Denmark to Greece, and the same cow from Holland to Portugal. The use of chemicals, fertilisers and hormones to sustain this unsustainable production will certainly expand, while regionally adapted and genetically diverse crop varieties and animal races will be forced into extinction.

In the animal sector, the CAP 'logic' is atrocious, as farmers are further pushed to separate milk and meat production, which means mixed breeds will be slaughtered as 'illogical'. With the drop in beef prices, specialised beef producers get a premium of 90 ECUs for each animal. Dairy farmers, trying to sell their unproductive cows, get nothing apart from falling beef prices. And with the drop in milk prices, the dairy farmers have no choice but to intensify further. This vicious price system will lead to an even deeper separation between meat and milk production, with each type of farmer trying to make it in his or her own sector, and write off any future for rustic, mixed breeds. There is no room for anything less than the pure and thoroughbred.

The 'accompanying measures' to promote some sustainable farming and nature conservation for the losers in the race will certainly not compensate the loss of diversity in the productive sector. The rule is intensification and uniformity, the exception is caring for the environment. The rule provokes extinction while the exception allows for conservation as long as there is money available. As the genetic resources community has slowly started to realise, the only way out of our spiral towards ever increasing genetic vulnerability on the farm is through the *integration* of production and conservation, rather than their separation. In this context, the last CAP reform is one giant step in just the wrong direction.

## *Agricultural policy: what reform?*

Hardly a week goes by these days without some report in the news about farmers protesting in the EC. The reform of the Common Agricultural Policy (CAP) threatens to put most of them out of a job, as prices will be further reduced in order to streamline the productive sector to a few competitive enterprises. At the same time, consumers are growing more critical and vocal about the quality of the food supply and how crops are grown and animals raised. Reports of nitrate overloads in soils and water supply, hormones in meat, chemical residues and heavy metals in fruits and vegetables are stirring up concerns about how wonderful all this cheap food really is.

The single largest factor shaping the direction of farming and of our food system is agricultural policy, which in the EC countries boils down today to the reform of the CAP, agreed upon by the 12 Agricultural Ministers on 21 May 1992. Hailed by the press as '*the most radical overhaul of the Common Agricultural Policy in its 30-year history*'[1], the CAP reform takes the industrialisation of agriculture one major, and perhaps final, leap forward. At the heart of the plan is a new, enigmatic and radical split of agriculture into the 'productive' and 'non-productive' sectors. 'Real' farming will be reserved for the most machine-like factories of northern Europe. These are the most intensified units producing food stuffs in an environment where cows stand on cement floors and lettuce is grown in nutrient solutions. Those producing under these conditions will be the only ones who might be able to chase over the price cuts to compensate income loss by increased volume of output. The few farmers that will be able to keep up – perhaps 20 to 25 per cent according to some calculations – will be the ones where productivity-raising technologies will be directed, accumulated and concentrated.

All the rest, about 75 per cent of our farms today, according to the same estimates, will be slated into the 'non-productive' sector, and with it most of southern Europe. On to these people and these regions, Brussels will initially sprinkle a rather fatal dose of payments and compensations to leave agriculture altogether or receive annually scrutinised subsidies for providing 'other services': landscape management, agro-tourism or ecologically benign earth-scratching. Obviously, nobody knows how long these subsidies will last. The next reform might have to take care of them.

The picture looming over European agriculture is one of a profound split. Quantity and output will be the realm of the productive sector, promoted and protected by the hardcore Ministries of Economic Affairs and Agriculture. Quality and diversity will be the job of the eco-service sector, weakly backed up by Ministries of Environment or Social Affairs. Such a division is a disaster in terms of safeguarding and using genetic diversity. Paying people to conserve outside of production systems is like inviting a hangman to cure your stiff neck. Diversity does not thrive in deep sleep. It must live and grow, or it dies out. Separating conservation from production – paying a few farmers to produce and compensating all the others for managing the environment – will only exacerbate the social and environmental problems that previous policies created.

The division is also a disaster for the 'productive' sector itself. The question is really what type of agriculture we want – and how long it should last. Do we want to go on diminishing the capacity of our farmlands and livestock to carry the load of exploitation with sophisticated and expensive external technologies, that tend to pollute as much as marginalise the role of people? Do we want to continue heightening the risks attached to the vulnerability of genetically uniform plants and animals? Do we want our agriculture to revolve around an ever declining number of species and varieties, with the same food produced everywhere and controlled by a few interest groups? Or on the contrary, do we want to see diversity come back to the farmlands and markets, and strengthen the balances and security force of our cropping systems, rural economies, relations with developing countries and personal lives? We have the choice.

Diversity, both social and biological, will have to be reinstated into production systems and the relationships that animate our rural and urban societies. Forcing the already intensified and genetically impoverished super-farms into a deepening spiral to produce more for less will push them further to the edge of biological disaster. A holistic and long-term strategy for agricultural development is more urgent than ever.

In sum, we are facing a proposed reform of Europe's agricultural system that amounts to no reform at all. It will concentrate the ills where they hurt most, within a reduced agricultural production scheme, letting the rest flounder under the banner of environmental and social difficulties. Clearly, if we want to create an agricultural strategy that is the slightest bit sustainable, in economic, environmental and human terms, then we have to take a more integrated approach. For as long as people will continue to produce food, by growing crops and raising livestock, production must be anchored within an explicit environmental and cultural framework.

The CAP desperately needs to be reformed, but in a direction that integrates the social and environmental dimensions of agriculture, those so-called 'externalities' that economists currently ignore. Genetic diversity is a vital component of both these dimensions. It is a cultural heritage that designs our societies and which people need to be able to continue moulding, and it is a tool to reform agricultural practices towards more viable forms of production. The cultural uniformity and the environmental damages of chemical farming are both inextricably linked to genetic erosion. We need an agricultural development programme that aggressively reintroduces diversity into our fields, markets and lives. In short, we have to reinstate diversity as a social strategy for survival.

Europe's agricultural policy should call upon those institutions that are storing the remaining folk varieties and landraces to get them growing again in the fields, and provide mechanisms to make that possible. Diversifying agriculture, and our agro-ecosystems at large, must start by putting a wider range of varieties into the production system. Heterogeneous landraces, multiline varieties, varietal mixtures and multiple cropping systems have to be developed and readapted to pull farming out of its spiral towards sterility and bankruptcy. This would be of benefit to the farmers, who could substantially improve the economic and ecological viability of their farms by having renewed access to crop varieties that are hardy, resistant, stable and better tasting. And it would obviously be of benefit to consumers, who would have more choice and a less vulnerable and less polluting food system.

Conservation of folk seeds is doomed if it is delinked from production, and our farming systems are in dire need of diversification. The answer seems obvious. An agriculture that is sustainable needs to revolve around diversity and social control over resources to meet social demands. The imperative, then, is not to keep deepening the very dangerous split but to rebuild the relationships that allowed farming, and agri'culture', to evolve for all those years. That means getting the resources back on to the farms and giving people the space and capacities to keep working with them. Certainly, the idea is not to push the clock backward and make every farmer a breeder. But if we do not get the resources back into circulation and if we do not decentralise control and management of those resources, we continue on our spiral towards dependency and vulnerability.

## Legal policies: renegotiating rights and responsibilities

If our agricultural policies are in need of reorientation, so are the legal systems that affect management and the use of biological diversity. The rules and laws currently in force do everything to reduce competition in the seed market and stifle innovation in plant breeding. Legal tools and regimes governing the use of our genetic heritage are extremely powerful. But they must be transformed into creative measures that will promote responsible action with respect to conservation, social control and exploitation of our plant heritage.

The two sets of laws governing the use of genetic resources – seed registration systems and intellectual property regimes – must be revised urgently to diversify the seed supply and balance monopoly rights with a clear set of obligations.

Regarding seed registration, it is urgent for national governments and the European Community to relax the very stringent laws that determine who can sell which seeds in Europe and what criteria they have to meet. The need to register varieties on a list before being able to commercialise them is not a bad idea, but the problem lies in the requirements to get them on the list: all geared towards uniformity.

The current registration system works against genetic diversity, and its use in agriculture, in at least two ways. First, as explained earlier, the criteria for certification do not allow for the legal marketing of traditional varieties and anything less than highly pure, elite cultivars. This effectively outlaws the entire spectrum of folk varieties, and thus hampers the efforts of people working with them. Second, even if criteria for registration were loosened to allow for more diverse planting materials to be marketed and offered to growers, fee levels would have to be cut. Current charges to get and keep a variety on the list are prohibitive for the many grassroots organisations that might be interested in doing so. *(See pages 59 and 109)*

Several official people working on genetic resources conservation for their governments know that this is a biased system and some administrators are starting to recognise it as well. There is every argument in favour of starting to redress this imbalance through the creation of an integrated seed supply system, also to the benefit of those farmers and gardeners that want to use more diverse materials. France has already set the example in the fruit sector, to show what can be done. Their parallel list for old fruits is less demanding in genetic purity and cheaper to comply with. Such examples are worth broadening, and should be extended to all species where registration is currently necessary. Where we are cursed with biased legislation that works against diversity, we must amend it. Current initiatives to introduce stricter EC legislation over fruits and flowers, to match the rules governing agricultural and horticultural crops, go exactly in the wrong direction.

While fighting to change laws that effectively restrict competition and diversity in the first link of the food chain, we also have urgently to knock some reasonableness into the current schemes that grant intellectual property rights over plants. If, in the market, there is an urgent need to guarantee people's rights to sell seeds, then in the field, we need to assert farmers' rights to use and re-use them. The reform of the Plant Breeders' Rights system, as enshrined in the UPOV Convention of 1991, has already weakened many of the particularities that justified this system as 'adapted' to the needs of agriculture. In particular, the farmer's right to re-use seed harvested from a protected crop variety has been scrapped, reformulated as a farmer's privilege and will have to be decided upon at the national level. The strengthening of Plant Breeders' Rights is not only bad news for farmers, but also restricts activities in breeding, and thus affects consumers as well. One of the features of the UPOV system will not allow breeders to use each other's varieties freely if the results are genetically alike. This limitation on the free exchange of germplasm will undoubtedly result in fewer breeders being able to compete, which, in turn, is likely to result in more uniformity in the field.

Of course, the situation will be much worse if our governments give in to the heavy pressure from the biotechnology industry to allow for full-fledged patents on life forms. If permitted, patents in the breeding sector would have a dramatic effect on availability of genetic resources for crop improvement, benefiting only a few companies who can make a fortune on a few genes. While Plant Breeders' Rights may make it economically difficult for farmers to re-use seed from their own harvest, patents will make it downright unlawful. And as companies patent whole species, plant characteristics and major genes, they will be able to regulate competition with near perfection.

Whatever rights society decides to grant to the developers of technology, they should be balanced with obligations. In the control of genetic resources, which are so vital to food security worldwide and which depend to a large extent on the contributions made by farmers, a balance must be struck. NGOs working to secure a better basis for farming and food security are talking now about the need to establish legislation on Intellectual Property Obligations (IPOs) at national, regional and UN levels to ensure that there is a more equitable balance of responsibilities.

IPOs should reflect society's legitimate demands for sustainable agricultural development, a clean environment and food security. In the field of plant breeding and biotechnology, this would mean that rights holders would be asked to contribute to the management of biological resources by subscribing to a set of internationally recognised guidelines for sustainable breeding. Some preliminary ideas of what such guidelines could entail are provided in Box 5.1.

---

**Box 5.1:** Breeding for sustainable agriculture: IPOs

1 **Measures to promote genetic diversity**

   (a) *Diversification of breeding programmes*
   Plant and animal breeders should be required to broaden the genetic base of agriculture by utilising a wider range of germ-plasm than currently practised. Their programmes should be monitored and directed to help discourage extreme forms of monoculture and be directed toward the development of mixed cropping systems, multilines and varietal mixtures.

   (b) *Limitation on the wide-spread multiple use of single genes*
   With the new biotechnologies it becomes in principle possible to widely incorporate the same 'single-gene solutions' in many agricultural crops and livestock. Apart from further promoting genetic erosion, this would exacerbate vulnerability to pests and diseases. Regulations should be drawn up to prevent this.

   (c) *Establishment of Genetic Uniformity Ceilings (GUCs)*
   Governments should establish regional threshold limits on genetic uniformity to be respected by breeders. When a single variety occupies a certain percentage of that crop's acreage in a region, measures should be taken to restrict further sales of the variety, promote the use of alternative varieties in the same region, or oblige the breeder to contribute to regional conservation efforts.

---

## 2 Support for conservation

(a) *User's fee on biological diversity*

Plant breeders should be subject to a tax on the commercial value of their seed sales as a measure to support conservation of genetic resources. The funds should be spent on national and regional conservation programmes that involve both governmental and non-governmental organisations.

(b) *Support for an international fund for the conservation of genetic diversity*

Breeders enjoying intellectual property rights over plant material should contribute to the worldwide effort to manage genetic resources through multilaterally agreed payments to an international fund under the auspices of the UN.

## 3 Cooperating with the broader genetic resources community

(a) *Return what you take*

Duplicates of germ plasm samples collected in farmers' fields should be provided as well as information resulting from research on those materials. Codes of Conduct on collecting, such as the one now being worked on in FAO, should be turned into binding national legislation.

(b) *Offer what is not in use*

Plant breeders should make genetic resources currently not under trial freely available to researchers and community organisations.

(c) *Honour farmers' rights*

Breeders should respect the right of farmers to reuse seed from their harvest without being subject to royalty charges. Legislation should be developed to recognise the rights of the informal innovators who developed local varieties in the first place, involving direct payment, adapted research and other rights derived from the innovative activities of farmers.

*Source:* Developed jointly by GRAIN Staff and Board, to be published in the UN's *ATAS Bulletin VIII* (1992).

The demands for stronger and stronger monopoly rights over our genetic heritage have gone too far. There is no longer a balance between society's interests and those of intellectual property rights holders. As citizens dependent on the food supply and dependent on the availability of genetic resources for our food security, we have to have the common sense to start negotiating again on the basis of a give-and-take arrangement. A system of rights without corresponding responsibilities is no system at all.

## Democratising research

Perhaps the most daunting challenge in securing a sound basis for agricultural development in Europe is reshaping the structure and process of research. Science and technology not only have to be responsive to society's real needs, apart from mere profit margins, but also have to promote the role of people in innovation, rather than marginalise them. Western Europe once enjoyed a strong public research environment, but as explained earlier, this is being sold off to the private sector at an alarming pace. When corporate interests take command of the test tube, we must take a second look at what kind of control we are ceding to essentially uncontrollable interests.

A strong public research system working to design innovation in agriculture is absolutely vital in several respects. First, we cannot expect the private sector to do everything. In plant breeding over the past decades we have seen what this means. Industry is not interested in certain crops or types of farming that are not profitable in the short or medium term. This, however, does not mean we should deprive ourselves of those crops or those innovations. At the same time, the public sector should also provide some healthy competition to the private sector in the same field of work. We also need some margin of openness about what kind of research is carried out and mechanisms to share information, personnel and resources in a public structure. In essence, we need accountability and forms of innovation that are not driven by commercial interests alone.

But salvaging our public research sector from its own sell-out to corporate financiers is only part of the problem. We desperately need to revamp the very structure and direction of research so that the work agenda is decided by the end-users and people are empowered through the process rather than merely considered passive recipients of technology. In agricultural research, this reversal of the top-down approach is more necessary than ever. Local solutions to local problems have to be found through alliances between farmers, scientists, small-scale industrialists and consumers. Farmers in particular have for too long been cut off from institutional research. They obviously know their needs and problems best, and they have an important role to play in agricultural research. Farmers are – by necessity – innovators and experimenters, as well as entrepreneurs. Tapping into this source of creativity and recognising its value, would be of great benefit to promoting more responsive, 'real needs' research.

The bias against farmer-initiated and farmer-based research in Europe is nowhere clearer than in the ways that 'unorthodox' agricultural sciences, for example the work to strengthen the underpinnings of biodynamic production or permaculture, are totally marginalised by the official sector and the dominant doctrine. Yet these approaches to agricultural development are extremely fertile and anything but unreasonable. Ecologically, they are geared towards sound production methods that are both long term and holistic, with diversity as a hinge to sustainability. Socially, they are eminently popular approaches to research and experimentation that bring people into the process of innovation rather than shut them out.

No one is against cutting edge research. The problem is that people have been cut out of it. There is no social control over research in Europe, just 'temperament testing' of new technologies when they arrive packaged at our doorsteps. Take biotechnology, for example. A lot of public criticism has emerged from NGOs, farmers and consumers organisations and environmental groups about the directions and control, the safety and relevance, of this new and powerful bundle of techniques and how they are put to use. Many of these people have been unfairly labelled as Luddites and anti-science obscurantists. That is to look at the issue from the wrong perspective. What many public and professional interest groups are crying out for is some form of transparency and democratic decision-making over science and technology. That kind of dialogue, consultation and participation in research and development is simply absent.

Clearly, the current structure and direction of agricultural research in Europe is inadequate to face the need to involve society – and the different 'consumers' of technology – in planning, directing and evaluating how we put science to work for us. Alienating people from the research process creates a sterile intellectual environment and a culture of irresponsibility that can become explosive. Resources and the development of technology have to be shared more democratically so that people will invest in innovation, and not forever be expected just to swallow what they are sold.

**135**

## Investing in diversity

Our weakness in demanding, protecting and creating diversity will ultimately kill the fertility and innovation that diversity provides. Consumer consciousness about the value of diversity, what it has to offer in terms of taste, self-reliance, the way food is produced or how we will be able to adjust crops to new needs, is invisible today. It does not exist. People complain about how tasteless tomatoes have become and how boring the array of apples is, but how many shoppers know that there are alternatives? Only recently have we seen some supermarkets in France, for example, stun clients by putting white-skinned aubergines, purple-fleshed potatoes and fluorescent orange peppers on their shelves. But the decision to do so came from the top, in a move to attract and tantalise. People have simply lost touch with diversity, just as they have lost touch with production and producers, and are unaware of what they are missing, today and for the future.

Local conservation of folk varieties has to find its way into local economies if it is to thrive in the long-term. While assuring the supply is an immediate headache for most seed- and livestock-saving programmes, creating the demand through consumer education is equally essential. No amount of funds or research will legitimise genetic diversity conservation in a social vacuum. People have to learn to relate to the wider scheme of food production – the forces facing growers and the politics of plant breeding – if they are to use the power they wield in their wallets intelligently.

Given the risks and problems we are facing with respect to the current way we are 'managing' our plant genetic heritage, it is high time we launched a concerted effort between people's organisations (the informal sector) and government agencies (the formal sector) to take effective action. The agenda on the table before us can be summarised in three needs: cooperation, networking and building alliances.

The need for cooperation, both between NGOs and scientists and within both communities, has perhaps never been so painfully felt as now. Cooperation between the formal and informal sectors was hardly imaginable just a few years ago. It has taken much effort in dialogue, breaking down old prejudices, learning to listen and learning to see – and this must increase and continue – in order for people to recognise that there is a common job to be done. The need for cooperation is also being felt very painfully because government scientists and NGOs are all choked for resources. These are bad times for conservation. It is often said that you have be very optimistic to work for the management of genetic resources. It would seem that you also have to be something of a masochist.

Networking is another vital element, in that it provides a mechanism for cooperation where benefits can be multiplied and costs – be they human, financial or other – saved. Without networks, people are isolated from each other, cannot share experiences and are deprived of a more equitable sharing of resources and benefits. And if there is one particular characteristic of seeds, it is their propensity to travel and the irresistible need that people handling them feel to share them. Diversity does not sit still; it must be exchanged, move about, grow and evolve. This means that people need community structures within which to work with these fantastic resources.

Yet we have seen and said a thousand times: conservation does not succeed in a social vacuum. In developing the work sustainably to manage genetic diversity in a long-term perspective, the greatest challenge before us is to create the social demand for this diversity. Many consumers simply do not know what they are cut off from in terms of variety, choice, security and a sound sense of responsibility for our plant genetic heritage. Unless they participate in the effort, through their concerns and demands, conserving and using genetic resources will not find the legitimacy, nor the economic rationale, that we already know it is due. Alliance building between conservationists (scientists and NGOs) and users (farmers and consumers) is critical to the long-term success of this work.

Slowly, the idea seems to be infiltrating all parts of Europe that we need a more concerted approach to managing genetic diversity. Global environmental issues about biodiversity and tropical forests are high on political agendas. But they are also real issues at home. NGOs and farmers are starting to be seen as partners in conservation. From Prince Charles to rock groups, the ill effects of chemical agriculture have everyone talking and campaigning about sustainable development and low-input farming practices. It would almost seem only a question of sewing the pieces together. However, while the ground work has to get going without delay, it will take time to readjust the policies and economic interests that got us here in the first place.

### Strengthening the grassroots

The forces working against people's efforts to salvage and reintroduce genetic diversity into production in Europe are numerous and in no way easy to tackle. As we saw earlier, part of this is because our agricultural policies and programmes are structured in such a way that they exclude alternatives. Resources are available only for formally recognised research, especially those working in fancy biotech projects, while laws keep NGOs and folk varieties excluded and marginalised. The official conservation system is biased towards a simple seed museum mechanism with little space for broadening the strategy to include dynamic and decentralised on-farm maintenance of genetic resources entrenched in local economic development. Also, price policies and low consumer awareness of the options offered by our plant heritage reinforce the push toward greater uniformity, which debilitates NGO work to diversify our food systems and local economies.

Yet another part of the problem is due to the nature of grassroots development work in itself. People working on the ground often don't have the time or capacities to reach out beyond their immediate tasks and engage in various support activities that could strengthen their work and make it more effective in the long run. Documenting the activities, fundraising, experimenting and research, campaigning and lobbying to raise awareness or wrest changes in laws or policies are all very necessary, but few grassroots organisations have the time, money, the expertise or the personnel to do it and do it effectively. Time spent on computers, the phone or with the press is time not spent in the field.

Of all the hurdles and obstacles constraining the development of local conservation activities, an important one is people's sheer ignorance of each other's existence and activities. This is very much the case in Europe, with Spanish NGOs not informed of what is going on next door in France or Belgian groups having little contact with their Italian counterparts. But even at the national level, no country has a mechanism or platform that brings NGOs together in one form or another to exchange information, much less to promote cooperation and networking. Many groups are simply out on their own working in the relative obscurity of their regions. Although things have improved a little over the past few years, the general situation remains one of isolation. Last year when GRAIN organised a second European network meeting of NGOs active in the field of genetic resources, many of the grassroots conservation leaders that attended had still never met each other.

This lack of contact between the actors is a direct obstacle that will take time and resources to overcome. Unlike the formal sector, the problem is not so much that it would lead to a duplication of effort. Strangely enough, while genebanks enjoy the benefit of established relationships and permanent contacts, they still duplicate their work. Their collections and research programmes often overlap. Not so in the informal sector.

Few grassroots collections double each other and it is usually limited to a few vegetables. Most of them are working with very local varieties, although many also conserve and offer popular old cultivars that have spread and been enjoyed in many European countries. A few months ago, we participated in the first encounter between the Tuscan and Provençal regional programmes to discuss respective work and possibilities for cooperation. Despite the fact that they are close neighbours, the French group had no experience in vegetables, which was the Tuscan *forte*, and the Italians had not worked on fruits, the area of French specialisation.

Recognising how vital communication is to develop the work of the informal sector, HDRA has recently taken upon itself to publish a newsletter for the grassroots conservation community in Europe. *Leaflet* is meant to provide a platform for information exchange and foster a sense of community among NGOs working in the field. While this is a valiant effort, there is only enough money to print it in English. When you sum it up, this absence of links among grassroots organisations means that networking and cooperation is very limited for the moment. There is simply no infrastructure to allow for building alliances, forging joint activities or developing the relationships to empower local organisations.

One of the most critical tools to develop right now in the NGO sector are mechanisms for regional networks in the different eco-cultural zones, where problems are common and language barriers are not a big hurdle. Regional networks would permit different groups to share their experiences and build upon them collectively. Engines are rolling right now to promote such cooperation and sharing in the Mediterranean region, focusing for a start on EC Mediterranean countries. NGOs in the region want to build a community approach to solving problems, such as social demand for diversity, and launching new projects, for example to share varieties and develop new products and markets together. Similar approaches could logically be pursued in other European regions and they are slowly germinating.

Pooling people and their experiences provides other opportunities. For example, joint activities could be undertaken with respect to media work, to get the message of the value of local diversity across to the public within a cross-cultural perspective. Regional seed exchange networks, trade unions of seed producers providing traditional or biodynamic seeds, and occasional diversity festivals or markets could also be developed. Perhaps most urgent is the need to create novel financial mechanisms to strengthen NGO work on genetic resources, for example through ethical banking or collective fundraising.

But the point is not only to focus on what to conserve and how best to go about it, but also to link up more energetically with farmers' organisations – particularly biological producers – to carry out on-farm research and develop new crops and production strategies. This is really where grassroots conservation could bloom as a sound alternative to genebanks or nature parks: directly as part of sustainable production systems and to promote innovation in this field. As biological producers often have special marketing structures, consumer awareness of diversity could be heightened through these channels in the most creative ways.

The financial restrictions known to the genebank sector are also too well known to NGOs. But while genebanks receive enough money to try to keep the collections alive, grassroots organisations barely have that much at all. Sources of funding for local conservation work in Europe are limited to membership fees, publications sales and seed sales – if and when these exist. Where they don't, most of the work is financed by voluntary labour. Only in the case of regional programmes is there some money available from local governments. And of course it often remains unlawful to sell seeds of unregistered varieties and recoup maintenance costs for most crops in Europe.

So long as grassroots conservation efforts remained embedded in such a political, scientific and economic ghetto, their effective contribution will be constrained and limited. But while funds to keep collections alive are the most urgent need, the greatest long-term hurdle to the efficiency of local management of genetic resources is the lack of economic and social demand for diversity. European society is continuously being structured against diversity. Obviously, this is the underlying logic of the European Community's long-term goal: one currency, one foreign policy, one decision-making body – and one kind of food system to feed one kind of consumer.

The direct link between conservation and valorisation of genetic diversity can really only be made at the local level, where there are specific production problems to face, markets to serve, cultures to develop and a heritage to relate to. Individual organisations can never carry out the task alone; it is too huge. Regional networks and practical alliances with farmers and consumers are vital to give diversity a meaning in our food system.

The basis of getting our crop management act together will have to be through improving the work of local organisations and their programmes to conserve and utilise genetic diversity directly in the regions. Just as there is no room for complacency in watching genetic erosion advance, there is no room for despair either in trying to overcome the obstacles to sustainable use and conservation of that diversity at the grassroots level.

## Bridging the gaps

The prospects in Europe for cooperation between our government genebanks, on the one hand, and grassroots organisations and the farming community, on the other, are certainly there and could benefit both sectors dynamically. The recognition that saving seeds solely in the deep sleep of cold storage is neither the best nor the only way to move forward is becoming more widespread. We even hear administrators grumble increasingly at new formal sector funding proposals. Genebanks will increasingly have a tough time trying to justify their work unless they find better forms of working with users and fellow managers of our genetic heritage. At the same time, NGOs could broaden their repertoire of botanical goods and build their capacities in developing and using alternative crops with the help of the formal genetic resources community.

NGOs are not only cut off from each other, but also pretty much cut off from official conservation programmes. The way things are set up today, it is simply not the job of government genebanks or national programmes to take on-farm maintenance of genetic diversity into account, either passively or actively. Many government programme leaders consider grassroots seed saving as something subversive if not simply so amateur and unprofessional that it is not worth considering as a valid option or contribution to 'the cause'. Several NGOs have had the unfortunate experience of knocking on genebank doors to request samples of materials to grow out, investigate and use in their programmes, only to be rejected with one excuse or another. Not enough seeds, request too imprecise, or NGOs are just not the 'bona fide scientists' that genebanks consider credible partners in conservation.

This results not only in limited access to materials, from both sides, but also to there being no relevant research that could strengthen grassroots conservation and breeding activities. Genebank protocols, grow-out strategies, methodological research and characterisation work is all geared toward *ex situ* conservation and the needs of professional plant breeders. This means that NGOs are strictly on their own to develop adapted descriptor lists, on-farm conservation and evaluation techniques, small-scale rejuvenation strategies and experimental breeding for low external input agriculture. Sometimes genebanks do offer back-up space for cold storage of NGO collections. While this is a help in case of emergencies, it only alleviates the problem of scientific marginalisation rather than attacking it.

More than anything, the genebank/NGO divide reflects an obscurantist type of mentality based on a lack of understanding that fortunately is slowly starting to change. Some people in official circles are coming to realise that NGOs pursuing local conservation work are not trying to undermine or replace the back-up seed bank option. On the contrary, they are trying to complement it with desperately needed alternatives, especially at the level of local production and agricultural development today, rather than tomorrow. NGOs have also yet to be convinced that government genebanks are doing a good job of conserving diversity and serving a useful purpose.

While mistrust and distrust can only be mended very slowly, it is becoming increasingly clear that the room for synergy is great. NGOs can help genebanks grow out national or regional collections and participate in on-farm evaluation trials, while genebanks can offer training, research support and back-up space. Surveys, documentation and collecting of materials could also be improved if the two sets of actors worked in conjunction rather than in isolation. The problem is that national structures and policies are impeding this search for dialogue and cooperation. When genebanks talk to NGOs it is often in the dark, on the side, a deviation from accepted practices. But once the talking starts, it tends to grow, not regress. The genebank people at Wellesbourne are developing closer relations with HDRA. The French national programme leaders are keen on legitimising and cooperating with NGOs in France. In Spain, the national genebank director recently sat down with grassroots NGOs in Catalonia and discovered it was possible to talk about joint activities with people he thought were enemies. The Dutch programme is also optimistic about room for collaboration with NGOs.

Perhaps the only European plant genetic resources programme that explicitly recognises the role of farmers and gardeners (although not their organisations) in local conservation is Greece. Their recently adopted national law foresees a place in the national effort for conserving Greek landraces where they were developed in the first place: within local farming systems, and preferably those not utilising chemicals for fertilisation, plant development or pest and disease management. The problem is that there is no money to implement the programme as ratified by the Greek Parliament. Other programmes, like France's and Switzerland's, have also started to adopt a wider and more holistic view to genetic diversity conservation but without backing it up with any formal political agreements and often without funds as well.

Linking up the two sectors will take time, but there is a wide enough range of activities to start exploring. In Mediterranean Europe and the former republics of the Soviet Union, there is urgent collecting work to be done. Farmers in these areas, from Portugal through Yugoslavia, into genetically rich Kazakhstan, continue to work with uncollected traditional cultivars of cereals, legumes and forage crops, not to mention fruits, nuts, medicinal plants and aromatics. Other areas, such as the coastal and mountain zones of Greece and Albania, also harbour a range of wild and intermediate forms useful for plant breeding. Genebank staff should attempt to involve grassroots organisations in identifying where these materials are and going to the field together to collect them. Whether these groups are already working on genetic resources or are simply trying to develop agriculture with local farmers does not matter much. The point is to involve local people in the endeavour, learn from them and teach them.

NGOs that go out hunting for old varieties also depend on local people and other groups to help them gather not only seeds or scions, but also popular knowledge about the plants: where they came from, what they are good for, how they are grown and enjoyed[2]. The cultural aspect of genetic resources can never be separated from the crops themselves. But few genebank staff are specialised in ethnobotany: how to survey, collect, interpret, maintain and value local knowledge about our plant heritage. Clearly, there are some important synergies that need to be developed in collecting what is left in the fields. Grassroots organisations would also benefit from the exposure and first hand understanding of what brought us to this stage.

Perhaps even more immediately and easier to set in motion would be what we would call 'Genetic Recovery Operations'. By this we mean rapid action to get traditional varieties and populations out of the confines of institutional storage units and growing again in the field, within farming systems. The best way to get materials out of the genebanks and into the farms is to organise national grow out programmes with NGOs, seed saving organisations, organic farming networks, schools and urban or rural gardening clubs. The advantage for the genebank is free labour in regenerating stocks: a job that has to be done but demands land, space and semi-skilled manpower that is not too hard to train. It would also liberate genebanks of the biological constraints that make growing out seeds of compatible species impossible at the same time. For local groups, it would provide access to indigenous

**143**

and exotic resources that are being withheld from them. Imagine the fun school children would have growing blue potatoes or white tomatoes for their national collection! In so doing, they would also learn about the South American cultures they came from, how they were developed and what their value is.

Few genebanks in Europe look beyond their own growing stations to rejuvenate materials. And not too many NGOs active in seed saving have had luck getting samples out of their government institutes. One exception to this is certainly Hungary. Hungary is perhaps the only country in Europe that has a firm strategy of growing out its seed collection in farmers' fields and gardens. Why? Because the staff know that if you grow out the plants in an alien environment, subject to different soils, climate or farming practices, you are likely to get a different result than you collected in the first place. So all Hungarian materials – ecotypes and landraces – are regenerated with farmers. Since the early 1960s, this 'back garden system', as they call it, has proven very effective and now involves more than one thousand different types of plant populations and several hundred farmers[3].

Despite 'the increasing spread of new agricultural practices' in Hungarian farmlands (i.e. the use of new varieties and chemicals), genetic resources programme leader László Holly, sharing views with us on how to progress, underscores a surprising result of farmer involvement that should have been deliberate. *'It is our most recent experience with this system, that as a "side effect", it has contributed to the reintroduction and spread of certain landraces which had earlier disappeared in the place of origin.'*[4] This is precisely the benefit that farming could and should derive from more dynamic relations with genebanks: reinstating diversity in production.

NGOs and formal sector scientists could develop joint research projects together, whether they touch upon strengthening grassroots conservation strategies or joint plant breeding programmes for sustainable agricultural development. This would be especially helpful to the biological farming movements in the regions, which need to develop new crops that have high qualities demanded by organic food consumers and health food stores. For example, innovating in mixed cropping, rotation systems or developing crops to stabilise and rehabilitate eroded soils could give rise to new ways of selling food to people and new products that carry with them an educational message about how the food was produced and why.

The Italian genebank is already working on this kind of approach in wheat. Rather than keep the traditional Italian emmers and spelts (often indistinctly called *farro*) in the fridge, they are working with farmers to reintroduce *farro* as an alternative to everyday modern wheat. Spelt is high in protein and can be used in bread-making for a different tasting and more nutritious result. It also brings farmers better income in Italy these days. But old varieties have to be further adapted to current conditions and threshing machines have to be adjusted to make spelt a viable option for the future[5].

What the Italian genebank may not know is that there are a range of small-scale farmers and NGOs who have long been working with *farro* in local farming systems throughout Italy. Why? For the high protein and other technical qualities, but mainly due to their adaptation and yield stability that modern wheats don't have. Had they gone to ask the NGOs keeping registers of what's going on at the grassroots level, they might have gained an entry into ongoing research in the field. In addition, a grassroots organisation in the former East Germany had already successfully developed free-threshing spelt as an alternative for small farmers in the GDR *(see page 106)*. International cooperation between genebanks and NGOs could also be useful!

There is a clear demand for genebank materials to get back into the fields and further adapted to local farming systems of today and the future. Those seeds are simply not around on the market. But at the same time, the formal system should involve local organisations in research and development work and adapt programmes to the needs of small-scale or organic farming, especially in marginal areas. If we are to consider genetic resources as a real heritage then there is a common interest in cultivating that heritage collectively.

Aside from all the different practical tasks that have to be initiated and developed between the formal and informal sectors to reinforce each other, there is also a need to conduct a dialogue on the policy issues affecting their work. If the disjointed actors in the conservation community came together, they could strengthen each others' demands for policy reforms affecting genetic resources management and resources to support the work. Switzerland has just initiated a national commission on plant genetic resources on which not just scientists but NGOs are sitting. Grassroots organisations have also been tentatively involved in the UK Steering Committee on Plant Genetic Resources, a body now under formalisation. These kinds of platforms for dialogue and discussion should be multiplied and seriously address policies and resources that are necessary for integrated conservation strategies and measures to secure them.

There is a lot that formal and informal actors have to learn and gain from each other. Cooperation will depend on a lot of factors, starting with trust, confidence and genuine interest, but it is more necessary than ever to strengthen the viability of genetic resources approaches – both to conserve for the future and to put into use today.

## Finding the support

The need for some kind of structural framework or programme to give direction and shape to this work in Europe, at governmental and intergovernmental levels, is obviously critical. National genetic resources programmes exist to a greater or lesser extent in most European countries, but as they stand now, local initiatives are rarely taken into account and there is little coordination between them. A parallel approach, then, would seem to be in order. National programmes should recognise the role and contribution of the non-profit, non-governmental sector in promoting conservation and use of biological diversity. This can only start when contacts are made, a survey of national NGO genetic resources work is carried out and local organisations have a say in national programme development.

But at the same time, Europe desperately needs an integrated pan-regional approach to genetic resources work. While a few crop networks linking genebanks for a handful of species are under development through the European Cooperative Programme, coordinated by IBPGR, this is an extremely limited and inadequate form of regional cooperation. European countries, governments and NGOs, should pool their experiences and resources to draw up a concerted framework for action. We need a common vision of where we are going with our genetic heritage in Europe, how we can help developing countries in the effort, a negotiated sense of priorities and a clear agreement on possible collaborative activities. Too much is done on an *ad hoc* basis between the most active countries, and this leaves many others behind. In addition, too little effort goes into addressing the substantive policy issues that are causing the genetic base of our economies and cultures to deteriorate in the first place. It is as if intellectual property matters and agricultural policies were a taboo that people are too intimidated to talk about.

Over the past couple of years, the only initiative to promote regional cooperation in Europe on a holistic basis has come from the European Parliament in Brussels. After years of fighting the apathy of the European Commission to do so much as lift a finger to support and promote

146

conservation and on-farm crop development, an aggressive proposal for an all-new programme and budget was adopted by the Parliament in late 1991. The proposal laid out a rationale for action in the field and at the policy level, to be guided by a group of national coordinators and active NGOs.

Encouraged by this initiative, genebank leaders, NGOs and IBPGR sat down and drew up a concerted proposal to feed into the development of the programme[6]. Yet, for reasons we can only guess, the Commission has been doing its best to delay any action on it. Less than two weeks after the budget line was adopted, we found ourselves in the office of the person within the Commission responsible for carrying out the programme. After ten excruciating minutes of explaining what an NGO was, the Commission representative finally looked like he understood. '*I get it! You're the private sector!*' Worse came when he gave his views on the programme proposal itself. '*I only heard of the term "genetic resources" a few months ago, at a Council meeting. I must admit the first thing I thought of was Hitler.*'[7] Lack of expertise or even the slightest ideas on what to do is obviously one reason why the Commission does not move forward. Distrust of an initiative coming from such a weird alliance of the Parliament, directors of genebanks and NGO activists, is certainly another one. Perhaps most disconcerting about the Parliament's proposal altogether, if you are a bureaucrat in Brussels, is the idea that it focuses not just on pumping up government genebanks, but also on the integration of the work of a totally unknown and uncontrollable informal sector.

Despite the Commission, the joint formal/informal sector proposal for a European programme is catching on and may eventually be set up. The real problem though is whether it makes sense to set up an EC programme when Europe, and especially the trouble facing Eastern Europe, is the main issue. It would certainly be beneficial in all senses for the EC to use this moment to really get its act together and take genetic resources, and their role in agricultural development, seriously. Community funding should be made available not to forever promote uniformity and erosion, but to put something into the long-term management of diversity.

But we would also like to see the EC initiative serve as a catalyst for a truly European-wide programme, involving other funding partners and agencies, such as the Council of Europe, the UN Development Programme, IBPGR and FAO. The point is that something has to start somewhere, so let it be the EC. But coordinated action and a platform for policy discussion at the supranational level covering all of Europe is vitally necessary. The EC would be extremely unwise to use this momentum to shut itself off. On the contrary, with growing recognition that biodiversity in general, and genetic resources in particular, are a global resource implying global responsibilities to manage it, Europe at large has to find a concerted rationale for investing in the conservation of what it exploits and in helping Third World farmers, the original plant breeders of the vast majority our crops, get a better role in and share from the system as well.

# Annex I: The genes in the bank

So what, in fact, are European genebanks conserving? A crucial question, but a very difficult one to answer. There is really no one central source of information on European genebank holdings. Wouldn't the EC coordinate such listings for their member states? No way. How about FAO? Neither. Individual governments? Sometimes. Last year the UK's then National Coordinator for Plant Genetic Resources, Andrew Cahn, wrote to GRAIN thanking *us* for informing *him* of Britain's 5,000 Phaseolus beans being safeguarded from extinction in a refrigerator at the University of Cambridge.

The best source of facts we could find on what and how much is in the banks was IBPGR and the databases they are slowly building up. However, the databases are incomplete, never totally up to date and sometimes hold erroneous or 'best guess' information. All the same, IBPGR has made the boldest effort to date to collect the information on what's in store. He was new to the job, but still. . .

The genebank gurus of today tell us that there are about three and a half million seed samples in storage in more than 100 countries. Of this, over one-third, nearly 1,240,000 samples, is sitting in Europe. The figures in IBPGR's database add up to just over a million, but we took those figures and went and talked to the genebank directors throughout the region to get their updates. These numbers are something of a moving target, it seems. Accessions come and go, depending on the banks' activities.

For example, at the end of the 1970s, the Gatersleben genebank in East Germany had about 44,000 accessions in stock. By the late 1980s, the figure had reached over 60,000. Today, Gatersleben maintains 95,000 samples of seeds, the third largest single collection in all of Europe. By comparison, through the exact same time period, West Germany's collection has not changed from its 52,000 specimen stock. The Russian food germplasm store is also growing, although Russian food stores have been having their problems. In 1941, when Vavilov was dying in prison, the germplasm collection he left behind had already tipped the 187,000 mark. Today the figure is reaching 370,000. Next week it may be even higher, as it seems they are still counting. Over the years, the Soviets have apparently imported more seeds than computers.

Of the one million plus seed samples in storage in Europe, well over 700,000 are in Eastern Europe (*graph 6*). This huge imbalance obviously represents past and present political priorities. While the EC houses the major breeding industries in the world, only a meagre one-third of Europe's crop heritage under institutional care is held by the EC countries. If we add in the other West European countries, the West to East ratio in genetic control is four to six. Thus, in the top ten ranking, only four West European countries make it: Federal Republic of Germany, France, the UK and Italy.

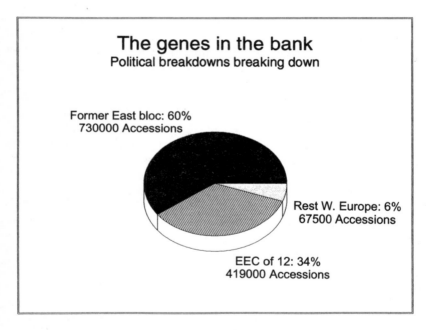

**Graph 6:** The genes in the bank: Political breakdowns breaking down

For those who want to know the details, we provide a full numeric count of germplasm holdings in 27 European countries in Table A.1 below. Let us insist: these numbers should in no way be taken as the golden

**Table A.1:** European genebank holdings by country in 1991

| Country | Accessions | % of total |
|---|---|---|
| Former USSR | 370,000 | 29.9% |
| France | 100,000 | 8.1% |
| Former East Germany | 95,000 | 7.7% |
| United Kingdom | 90,000 | 7.3% |
| Italy | 73,000 | 5.9% |
| Poland | 60,000 | 4.8% |
| Romania | 52,000 | 4.2% |
| Former W. Germany[1] | 52,000 | 4.2% |
| Hungary | 45,000 | 3.6% |
| Czechoslovakia | 44,000 | 3.6% |
| *TOP TEN* | *981,000* | *79.2%* |
| *Others* | | |
| Bulgaria | 40,000 | 3.2% |
| Spain | 38,000 | 3.1% |
| Former Yugoslavia[2] | 33,000 | 2.7% |
| Nordic countries[3] | 24,000 | 1.9% |
| Netherlands | 20,000 | 1.6% |
| Albania | 16,000 | 1.3% |
| Turkey | 14,000 | 1.1% |
| Belgium | 13,000 | 1.1% |
| Switzerland | 11,000 | 0.9% |
| Portugal | 11,000 | 0.9% |
| Sweden | 8,500 | 0.7% |
| Greece | 7,000 | 0.6% |
| Denmark | 6,000 | 0.5% |
| Finland | 5,000 | 0.4% |
| Austria | 5,000 | 0.4% |
| Ireland | 4,000 | 0.3% |
| Cyprus | 800 | 0.1% |
| Norway | 700 | 0.1% |
| TOTAL EUROPE | 1,238,000 | 100% |

*Notes:*
(1) Includes the Dutch-German potato and beet collections
(2) Genebank under construction, but current situation unclear
(3) Collectively managed at the Nordic Genebank in Sweden

*Source:* Compiled by GRAIN from IBPGR databases and consultations with National Coordinators of Plant Genetic Resources Programmes in Europe

truth, but we did our best to try to compile an approximate picture of the size of collections.

If we break down Europe's genebank holdings by crop, the picture is not too surprising. Over half of what is in store for farming's future are cereals, followed by the pulse crops people eat (13 per cent), and vegetables (11 per cent) (*Graph 7*).

With regard to the species European farmers and gardeners have long been cultivating and developing, cereals, legumes and forage crops score highly in genebanks today. Among our horticultural heritage, the cabbages, onions, beets and carrots have caught the eye of government officials, but a paltry number of distinctly European vegetables like parsnip, endive, artichoke, salsify and asparagus are being conserved. The same goes for culinary herbs and medicinal plants, which despite Europe's wealth in diversity seem to be grossly neglected. One need only visit the Mediterranean areas of France, Spain or Italy to witness the omnipresence and widespread use of heady aromatic and medicinal plants like lavender, thyme, basil, tarragon and sage. These plants are not only well adapted to the dry summers of southern Europe, they provide sustenance for pollinators such as bees and are an excellent source of essential oils for a whole range of industries: food, cosmetics, medicines, and perfumed goods.

Olive and grape also score poorly. Despite their long history, and economic importance for Mediterranean agriculture, we only found 317 accessions of grape and no more than 46 samples of olive in the European system! We can also wonder where the stocks of some important native European crops are altogether. Plants like hop, saffron and carob, which were domesticated and developed in Europe and are in no way obsolete crops, are not registered in our governments' genebank systems at all!

It is likely in many cases that the 'missing crops' are being kept, but the government responsible has not informed IBPGR. For instance, it is common knowledge that the Polish germplasm system is conserving indigenous hops for their brewing industry. And the Netherlands is definitely withholding information from the world's germplasm registers. Anyone who has visited the Dutch genebank in Wageningen can't help but notice the impressive hemp plants thriving in the greenhouses. Hemp was one of the earliest crops cultivated in Europe for its oils and fibres. Today it is grown for producing marijuana and its consumption is tolerated in the Netherlands. Yet this obvious collection is not reported to IBPGR. The same goes for Ethiopian crops. We once showed a listing of Ethiopian germ plasm being held in the Netherlands – as reported in the world crop databases – to Jaap Hardon, Director of

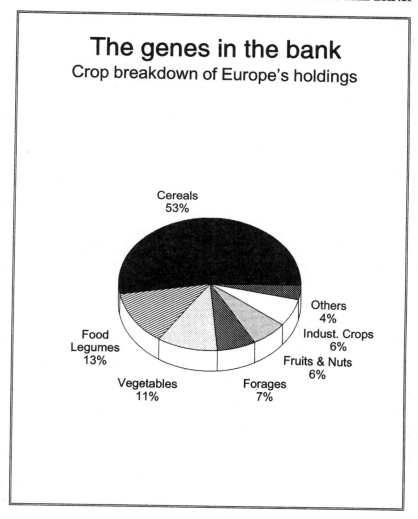

# The genes in the bank
## Crop breakdown of Europe's holdings

Cereals
53%

Others
4%

Indust. Crops
6%

Fruits & Nuts
6%

Food
Legumes
13%

Vegetables
11%

Forages
7%

**Graph 7:** The genes in the bank: crop breakdown of Europe's holdings

the Dutch genebank. Hardon looked at the numbers and laughed – he had much more Ethiopian material than that.

We did what we could to turn IBPGR's technical databases into something an ordinary person can understand. It was no easy task. For what it is worth, what follows is a detailed listing of Europe's stored germ plasm by crop, as registered by 1991.

**Table A.2:** The genes in the bank: Europe's genebank holdings by crop (1991)

| | |
|---|---:|
| *Cereals and grains* | *554,403* |
| Wheat | 254,577 |
| (*of which wild*) | *9,783* |
| Barley | 138,804 |
| (*of which wild*) | *15,831* |
| Maize | 52,417 |
| Oat | 34,136 |
| (*of which wild*) | *2,133* |
| Millets and sorghum | 31,457 |
| Rice | 18,413 |
| Rye | 9,974 |
| Triticale | 8,657 |
| Buckwheat | 4,807 |
| Quinoa | 965 |
| Cereals | 106 |
| Teff | 55 |
| Grain Amaranth | 35 |
| | |
| *Food legumes* | *135,891* |
| Pea | 38,444 |
| French bean | 23,875 |
| Misc. *Phaseoleae spp.* | 20,076 |
| Lupin | 13,686 |
| Vetch | 13,290 |
| Broad bean | 11,666 |
| Chickpea | 6,843 |
| Lentil | 5,535 |
| Winged bean | 703 |
| Runner bean | 533 |
| Misc. *Vigna spp.* | 419 |
| Cowpea | 331 |
| Lima bean | 224 |
| Tepary bean | 151 |

| | |
|---|---|
| Mung bean | 74 |
| Hyacinth bean | 15 |
| Mat bean | 7 |
| Yam bean | 7 |
| Sarawak bean | 4 |
| Pigeon pea | 4 |
| Sword bean | 2 |
| Hog pea | 2 |

| | |
|---|---|
| *Vegetables* | *112,152* |
| Cruciferous crops | 23,770 |
| Tomato | 18,765 |
| *(of which wild)* | *44* |
| Cucurbits | 17,650 |
| Peppers | 14,373 |
| Onion family | 9,283 |
| Beet | 6,609 |
| *(of which wild)* | *683* |
| Lettuce | 6,539 |
| Misc. vegetables | 5,975 |
| Carrot | 3,335 |
| Aubergine | 1,957 |
| Spinach | 1,076 |
| Celery | 521 |
| False flax | 467 |
| Chicory | 328 |
| Fennel | 274 |
| Garden cress | 270 |
| Amaranth | 214 |
| Okra | 212 |
| Rocket salad | 178 |
| Parsnip | 135 |
| Burnet | 98 |
| Endive | 66 |
| Artichoke | 44 |
| Salsify | 6 |
| Asparagus | 3 |
| Red sorrel | 1 |
| Chinese rhubarb | 1 |
| Water cress | 1 |

Sorrel                                         1

*Forages*                                 *72,889*
Misc. forage grasses                       18,095
Clover                                     13,005
Broom corn                                 10,127
Alfalfa                                     9,108
Orchard grass                               5,444
Ryegrass                                    5,294
Fescue                                      4,655
Misc. forage legumes                        2,210
Chickling vetch                             1,705
Sainfoin                                    1,245
Trefoil                                       866
Bromegrass                                    820
Fenugreek                                     166
Misc. forages                                 106
Centrosema                                     31
Borage                                         12

*Fruits and nuts*                         *68,175*
Apple                                      16,174
Melons                                      7,139
Pear                                        6,550
Citrus fruits                               5,979
Peach                                       4,598
Misc. stone fruit                           4,456
Cherry                                      4,103
Plum                                        3,025
Hazelnut                                    2,885
Strawberry                                  2,407
Apricot                                     1,805
Fig                                         1,084
Pomegranate                                 1,031
Raspberry and blackberry                      919
Gooseberry                                    849
Almond                                        743
Walnut                                        701
Blackcurrant                                  555

| | |
|---|---:|
| Rose | 492 |
| Grape | 317 |
| Quince | 306 |
| Chestnut | 267 |
| Mulberry | 255 |
| Avocado | 215 |
| Watermelon | 207 |
| Red currant | 178 |
| Mango | 159 |
| Banana | 158 |
| Persimmon | 101 |
| Pistachio | 76 |
| Cranberry | 69 |
| Pineapple | 60 |
| Tatapian honeysuckle | 52 |
| Olive | 46 |
| Misc. tropical fruits | 40 |
| Pecan | 30 |
| Kiwi | 30 |
| Rowanberry | 28 |
| Elderberry | 20 |
| Juneberry | 17 |
| Medler | 11 |
| Custard apple | 9 |
| Guava | 8 |
| Huckleberry | 5 |
| Loquat | 5 |
| Avens | 4 |
| Tormentil | 3 |
| Jujube | 2 |
| Passion fruit | 1 |
| Macadamia nut | 1 |
| | |
| ***Industrial crops*** | ***67,968*** |
| Soybean | 21,558 |
| Sunflower | 10,826 |
| Cotton | 9,540 |
| Flax | 8,984 |
| Rape | 4,766 |

| | |
|---|---|
| Rubber | 3,400 |
| Sugarbeet | 2,219 |
| Groundnut | 1,948 |
| Castor | 1,649 |
| Sesame | 1,251 |
| Tobacco | 1,180 |
| Safflower | 434 |
| Hemp | 103 |
| Coffee | 82 |
| Jute | 28 |
| | |
| *Tubers* | *29,362* |
| Potato | 29,099 |
| (of which wild) | 539 |
| Taro | 110 |
| Yam | 52 |
| Jerusalem artichoke | 50 |
| Sweet potato | 46 |
| Misc. aroids | 5 |
| | |
| *Narcotics* | *4,009* |
| *Herbs & aromatics* | *1,779* |
| | |
| Coriander | 500 |
| Dill | 385 |
| Parsley | 378 |
| Basil | 200 |
| Caraway | 135 |
| Anise | 73 |
| Marjoram | 66 |
| Peppermint | 15 |
| Lavender | 12 |
| Thyme | 8 |
| Tarragon | 3 |
| Sage | 3 |
| Wormwood | 1 |
| | |
| *Medicinal plants* | *1,778* |

| | |
|---|---|
| *Miscellaneous* | *1,629* |
| Total | **1,050,035** |

*Notes:*

1. The sum total does not match current genebank holdings (1,238,000) as this table only covers those accessions properly described and reported to IBPGR as of 1991.

2. We used two sources to translate the Latin names of crops to their common name: *Plants and Plant Products*, FAO Terminology Bulletin 25/1, Rome, 1983, and A.C. Zeven and J.M.J. de Wet, *Dictionary of Cultivated Plants and their Regions of Diversity*, PUDOC, Wageningen, 1982.

3. Cruciferous crops include cabbages, radish, cauliflower, turnip, kohlrabi, rutabage, mustard plants, etc. Cucurbits include cucumbers, squashes, gourds and melons. The onion family is comprised of onions, garlic, shallots and leek. Narcotic crops in storage are essentially the opium poppy.

4. We listed soybean, sunflower and rape under 'Industrial Crops' as they are mainly grown for oil production.

5. We may have made mistakes in translating some legumes, grasses and members of the *Solanum* genus, due to problems with taxonomy and the lack of rigour in IBPGR's database.

6. Where possible we included crop relatives in the crop count.

# Annex 2: Addresses and contacts

For the formal sector, each European country – except for Luxembourg, Albania, Romania, and some of the emerging republics in the East – has a government-designated National Coordinator of its formal plant genetic resources programme. They act as representatives of their countries within the European Cooperative Programme (ECP/GR) and in international fora. They are supposed to serve as central clearinghouses for their country's institutional work on genetic resources conservation and can be approached for information, seed samples or advice.

As to the informal sector, NGOs, associations and individuals are multiple and scattered about. There are many groups of all sizes and natures working on genetic resources conservation and use at the grassroots level. Below, we only provide a brief smattering of the ones we have been in contact with as well as NGOs working on policy issues around genetic resources that can be contacted for further information about practical work at the national level.

Until an integrated European Directory of government agencies, NGOs and international groups engaged in local conservation in Europe is published, we can only provide incomplete information about who is doing what.

## National level

### Austria

*National Coordinator*
Dr Herman Redl
Federal Ministry of Agriculture & Forestry
Stubenring 1
A-1011 Vienna
Tel: (43-222) 7500

Austria has four small genebanks but they have never established constructive links with local gardeners and farmers working to preserve old varieties.

*NGOs*
Ms Nancy Arrowsmith
Arche Noah
Postfach 139
Margaretenstrasse 14
A-3500 Krems/Donau
Tel: (43-2732) 73 650
Fax: (43-2732) 74 037

Arche Noah was formed in 1990 through the fusion of two groups. Current membership exceeds 350 people in the German-speaking countries (Austria, Germany and Switzerland). Funding comes from membership fees, publication sales and personal sacrifice. Members are particularly busy collecting varieties that are threatened with extinction as they are removed from official catalogues in their countries. Arche Noah publishes its *Jahreskatalog*, an annual listing of varieties offered for exchange by its membership. In 1990, the *Allgemeine Gemüsefibel* was published. It provides a comprehensive listing of open-pollinated (non-hybrid) horticultural varieties still available but threatened by being dropped from the market. This catalogue is a form of early warning system for genetic erosion in the vegetable sector, for all those interested in salvaging our crop heritage from imminent extinction. Arche Noah is now preparing a German-language translation of *Seed to Seed*, a practical guidebook to seed saving in your garden published by the US-based Seed Savers Exchange. They have information about other groups active in Central and Eastern Europe.

## Belgium

*National Coordinator*
Mr R. Bienfet
Administration of Agronomic Research
Manhatten Centre, Office Tower
Ave. du Boulevard, 21 (7ème etage)
B-1210 Brussels
Tel: (32-2) 211 72 11
Fax: (32-2) 211 72 16

The Belgian programme is sympathetic toward the need to integrate the work of both government-sponsored public research institutes and popular initiatives to conserve genetic resources. Some government institutes have experience working with the public to collect and conserve fruit species and raise awareness through the media about the value of genetic diversity.

*NGOs*
CRABE
Rue Saint Medard, 4
B-1370 Jodoigne
Tel: (32-10) 81 40 50
Fax: (32-10) 81 42 50

CRABE promotes research and development work on biological food production in Belgium and is very interested in the aspect of genetic resources.

Mr Gilbert Cardon
Fraternité Ouvrière
58, rue Charle Quint
B-7700 Moucron
Tel: (32-56) 33 38 70

Fraternité Ouvrière is a workers' solidarity movement that promotes urban gardening. They are reportedly using and maintaining some 1,200 vegetable varieties through this work.

Mr Marek Posnanski
Collectif Stratégies Alimentaires
Quai du Commerce, 9
B-1000 Brussels
Tel: (32-2) 218 47 27

CSA works on a whole range of policy issues affecting sustainable development, including genetic resources and biotechnology. Contact for further information about groups working in the field in Belgium.

### Bulgaria

*National Coordinator*
Dr D. Stoyanov
Institute of Plant Introduction & Genetics Resources 'K. Malkov'
Sadovo

4122 Plovdiv
Tel: (359-32) 2221

*NGOs*
Mr Jordan Danchev
Bulgarian Society for the Conservation of the Rhodope Mountains
2 Gargarin Street
1113 Sofia
Tel: (35-92) 70 51 78
Fax: (35-92) 70 54 98

Jordan's organisation is working at the grassroots level to assure the sustainable economic development of Rhodope Mountain area based on the region's rich genetic and cultural heritage.

## Cyprus

*National Coordinator*
Dr C.S. Serghiou
Agricultural Research Institute
Ministry of Agriculture
PO Box 2016
Nicosia
Tel: (357-21) 30 51 01
Fax: (357-21) 44 51 56

## Czechoslovakia

*National Coordinator*
Dr Ladislav Dotlacil
Research Institute of Plant Production
Ruzyne 507
161 06 Prague 6
Tel: (42-2) 36 08 51

*NGOs*
For information about people's efforts to hold on to old breeding stocks and landraces in this country, please contact Pro Specie Rara and Arche Noah (addresses elsewhere in this listing). PSR has an office in Prague to coordinate emergency efforts in the animal sector, while Arche Noah is in contact with a range of environmental organisation, researchers and others concerned by genetic erosion – wipeout is perhaps the word – of plants and animals in Czechoslovakia.

## Denmark

*National Coordinator*
Dr Arent Josefsen
Danish Institute of Plant and Soil Science
Skovbrynet 18
DK-2800 Lyngby
Tel: (45) 93 09 99
Fax: (45) 93 08 19

The Danish programme is interested in carrying out research with crop genetic diversity to suit ecologically sound farming systems.

*NGOs*
Mr Heine Refsing
Hvejselvej 127
DK-7300 Jelling

Ms Lila Towle
Drowten 9, Lindum
DK-8830 Tjele

Heine and Lila are members of the US-based Seed Savers Exchange and participate in a smaller national SSE. The Danish network has 50 members. They have recently found a 3rd generation 100-year-old pea landrace and continuously try to spread interest in old varieties. Heine runs an Ethnobotanical Garden on a public farm where he is engaged in crop development for alternative agriculture. He is collecting and introducing old or forgotten crops and carrying out research on their agronomic qualities. He has written articles about the value and use of old cultivars for Danish gardeners and is preparing a book on 'Breeding Strategies for Sustainable Agriculture', drawing from his practical experience with the rehabilitation of landraces in local farming systems.

## Finland

*National Coordinator*
Dr E. Kivi
Hankkijas Plant Breeding Institute
SF-04300 Hyryla

*NGOs*
Ms Anga Alanko
Maatiainen

Korsutie 34
SF-00370 Helsinki
Tel: (398-90) 55 72 63

Maatiainen is a grassroots organisation established two or three years ago to conserve and grow old Finnish crop varieties, especially fruits and flowers. They also work with vegetables such as onion species and, like SESAM in Sweden, would like to cooperate further with other NGOs in the Nordic and Baltic regions.

## France

*National Coordinator*
Dr André Charrier
Bureau des Ressources Génétiques
57, rue Cuvier
F-75231 Paris Cedex 05
Tel: (33) 47 07 15 75
Fax: (33) 45 35 70 15

The French programme is – morally, at least – supportive of any effort to contribute to conservation and utilisation of genetic diversity, including the work of local associations, gardeners and amateurs, but has a limited budget to carry out this work. The BRG has an administrative role in coordination and information, but does not run a genebank.

*NGOs*
Club Mémoire Verte
B.P. 20
F-33670 La Sauve

The 'Green Memory Club' is a membership seed exchange network. They publish an annual catalogue of landraces offered from members for members, a liaison bulletin for the network, technical sheets giving advice on seed saving and cultivation techniques for old varieties, and provide a range of other information supports. Through their efforts, over 400 rare varieties are being maintained in cultivation on the farm and in the garden. They have an experimental station that does varietal testing under production conditions. The network collaborates with professionals and scientists in France who are aware of the value of what these people are doing voluntarily.

Ms Sylvia Schmidt
Le Biau Germe
F-47360 Montpezat d'Agenais
Tel: (33) 53 95 08 92 (morning)
(33) 53 95 04 40 (afternoon)

Le Biau Germe is a family-run seed company devoted to maintenance and organic production of traditional varieties not found on the French National Catalogue of seeds legally marketable. Their high-quality seeds are available exclusively by correspondence, in small portions for backyard growers. Every year they publish a catalogue of their offerings, including vegetables, grains, herbs, flowers and green manure crops – mostly very old, well-proven French folk varieties but also some exotic introductions for those who seek diversity!

Mr Philippe Marchenay
CNRS
Alimentec Technopole de Génie Industriel Rhône-Alpes
6, place de la Grenouillère
F-01000 Bourg-en-Bresse
Tel: (33) 74 45 30 44
Fax: (33) 74 24 61 33

Dr Marchenay is an ethnobotanist carrying out research on the cultural links between plants and people, focused on Europe's traditional crops and livestock. He has produced books and articles on conserving genetic resources at the grassroots level and is currently establishing a European network of researchers active in this field.

Mr Georges Gueutal
Les Croqueurs de Pommes
Cité des Associations
B.P. 702
F-90020 Belfort cedex

A voluntary organisation with over 2,000 members in France, Belgium, Germany, Switzerland and Italy devoted to conserving traditional fruit stocks from genetic erosion at the local level. Aside from members' own collections managed in backyards and gardens, the organisation has established 25 'orchards of salvation' across the French countryside, harbouring 2,500 individual fruit varieties. 'The Apple Munchers' publish a trimestrial newsletter for their network.

Mr Philippe Barret
GEYSER/PAGE PACA
rue Grande
F-04870 St. Michel l'Observatoire
Tel: (33) 92 76 62 44
Fax: (33) 92 76 65 50

GEYSER is an active member of PAGE PACA, a regional genetic resources programme involving INRA, botanical gardens, NGOs, schools, local chambers of agriculture, etc. in southeast France. Since 1984 they have carried out inventories, public awareness campaigns, and training and are working to help diversify agriculture in the region based on the rehabilitation of locally-adapted crops and animals for sustainable farming systems. Can provide contacts with the hundreds of French associations working on genetic conservation and use.

*Germany*

*National Coordinators*
Dr Manfred Dambroth
Institute für Pflanzenbau und Pflanzenzuchtung (FAL)
Bundesallee 50
D-W-3300 Braunschweig
Tel: (49-531) 59 63 65
Fax: (49-531) 59 63 07

Dr Karl Hammer
Director
Institute für Pflanzengenetik und Kulturpflanzenforschung (IPK)
Correnstrasse 3
D-O-4325 Gatersleben
Tel: (49-39482) 50
Fax: (49-39482) 5286

*NGOs*
Mr Ludwig Watschong
VEN
Ahornweg 6
D-W-3525 Arenborn
Tel: (49-5574) 1345

VEN stands for 'Vereins zur Erhaltung der Nutzpflanzenvielfalt' or Network for the Conservation of Crop Diversity. Over 60 people are actively engaged in the network, run by Ludwig Watschong. They are multiplying and exchanging old crop varieties of interest to gardening and farming. Constrained by lack of resources, the network nevertheless wants to expand and welcomes new members who care about diversity and want to help maintain old varieties alive and in use at the local level.

Mr Peter Raatsie & Martin Bossert
Pflanzenzuchtverein
Wernstein 24
D-W-8653 Mainleus
Tel: (49-9229) 8157

An independent research organisation maintaining a large collection of old local varieties for research and development of biodynamic production and conservation methods. Through breeding and agronomic trials carried out with small farmers, they are adapting old crops to farming systems that produce high quality food in harmony with the environment and promoting farmer control over resources and production systems.

Dr Jürgen Reckin
Gessellschaft für Ökolgische Pflanzenzucht
Altenhoferweh 1
D-O-1301 Werbellin
Tel: (37-371) 27902

An independent research organisation carrying out work on sustainable agriculture for small farmers in the former GDR. Jürgen and his colleagues had assembled quite a large collection of crop diversity and were using it to develop grains, forages, legumes and vegetables that were high in nutritional value, grew well without chemical inputs, could be processed easily on small holdings, were resistant to local pests and diseases, and provided a stability of yield. Despite their large collection of landraces, meticulously conserved through active use, and constructive breeding work, this operation was threatened with being shut down by the West German authorities. However, the station has recently been bought up to produce biological food, which Jürgen hopes may offer an opportunity to raise enough income to support conservation and breeding again.

## Greece

*National Coordinator*
Dr Athanassioioe Zamanis
Greek Gene Bank
PO Box 14514
GR-541 10 Thessaloniki
Tel: (30-31) 47 15 44
Fax: (30-31) 47 12 09

The Greek Parliament passed in 1991 a decree setting out a new structure for the national programme, but it has not been implemented for lack of funds. The new programme specifically recognises the role of farmers in promoting decentralised conservation and use of traditional Greek varieties by providing financial compensation to those growers who would cultivate landraces on their farms under traditional agricultural methods. On-farm conservation in the Greek programme would complement the genebank and *in situ* reserves.

*NGOs*
Prof. Dr Andreas Georgoudis
IDAAM
c/o Laboratory of Animal Husbandry
Faculty of Agriculture
Aristotle University
GR-54006 Thessaloniki

IDAAM is an independent effort launched by concerned public sector scientists on the side of their work to conserve traditional Greek farm animal breeds threatened by extinction due to the massive introduction of more uniform, 'high-yielding' ruminants from abroad.

Mr Dimitris Dimitriadis
Federation of Ecological Alternative Organisations
Politechnion 8
GR-10433 Athens
Tel: (30-1) 522 12 30

Dimitris is trying to stimulate NGO work in Greece on sustainable agriculture and would like to help develop on-farm conservation of genetic resources through alternative farming structures. Much of this work, though, has yet to get off the ground for lack of financial and human resources.

## Hungary

*National Coordinator*
Dr László Holly
Research Centre for Agrobotany
I.A.Q.
H-2766 Tápiószele
Tel: Tápiószele 41

Hungary's national programme actively involves farmers in the dynamic and decentralised maintenance of traditional Hungarian landraces. Through this direct contact between conservation and production, a number of old varieties, which otherwise might have sat still in the genebank, have been successfully reintegrated by rural communities into their farming systems.

*NGOs*
Mr Nick Vaczek
Environmental Programme
Central European University
URI U. 49
H-1014 Budapest
Tel: (36-1) 156 95 39

The Central European University is trying to strengthen local work on agriculture and the environment, including grassroots management of genetic resources. They are in touch with local groups from Hungary and other Central European countries and can be contacted for further information.

## Iceland

*National Coordinator*
Dr Gunnar Olafsson
Agricultural Research Institute
Keldnaholt
IS-110 Reykjavik

## Ireland

*National Coordinator*
Dr D.P. Feeley
Department of Agriculture
Kildare Street

Dublin 2
Tel: (353-1) 78 90 11, ext. 2031

*NGOs*
Ms Anita Oppenheimer-Hayes
Irish Seed Savers Network
Marley
St. Mullins
Co. Carlow
Tel: (353-503) 24444

A small but enthusiastic group busy building up a regional variety library.
Mr Charlie Spillane
University of Dublin
Department of Genetics
Lincoln Place Gate
Trinity College
Dublin 2
Tel: (353-1) 77 29 41
Fax: (353-1) 679 85 58

Charlie and his colleagues are keen on setting up a charitable trust in Ireland to promote grassroots conservation of plant and animal genetic resources and provide a common forum for policy work, information activities and lobbying towards Irish and EC authorities. Knowing that there are a lot of groups and individuals concerned about increasing genetic uniformity in Ireland, the need for a collective front and sharing of resources is a pressing one.

## *Italy*

National Coordinator
Dr Pietro Perrino
Istituto del Germoplasma (CNR)
Via G. Amedola 165/A
I-70126 Bari
Tel: (39-80) 58 34 00
Fax: (39-80) 558 75 66

The Italian programme is still collecting traditional landraces that can be found in marginal areas of Italy and is trying to develop alternative crops for today's farming systems based on rustic old varieties.

**171**

*NGOs*
Dr Giovanni Cerretelli
Bigallo Verde
Via Pellas 16
I-50141 Firenze
Tel: (39-55) 45 60 88
Fax: (39-55) 45 60 88

Bigallo Verde is a cooperative of agronomists working on environmental defence and organic farming together with other public organisations of Tuscany. Since 1986 they have been working with the regional government and University of Florence recuperating traditional varieties. They have collected over 200 samples of mostly horticultural crops. The regional government is now establishing a regional seedbank where they will be stored. The next stage of the project is to integrate the varieties into local farming systems and agricultural development work, but is pending for lack of funds.

Ms Maria Rosaria Perna
Via Mediterraneo 3/B
I-63100 Ascoli Piceno

Maria Rosaria, an agronomist, has launched a regional programme in Marche for *in situ* dynamic conservation of plant genetic resources, starting with fruits. She hopes to go into medicinal plants. The programme involves the regional government of Marche and local NGOs and farmers' organisations.

Mr Fabio Terragni
Gruppo di Attenzione sulle Biotechnologie
Via Iglesias, 33
I-20128 Milano
Tel: (39-2) 27 00 11 35
Fax: (39-2) 255 22 81

GAB is working on policy issues related to biotechnology and biodiversity. They have prepared an educational booklet for school children on genetic diversity and the food system and compiled a short analytical study on grassroots conservation of genetic resources in Italy, published in Lega Per l'Ambiente's *Ambiente Italia 92*, with a full listing of names and addresses. GAB is planning to carry out a full-fledged inventory of all genetic diversity conservation activities in Italy, both governmental and grassroots.

Mr Antonio Onorati
Centro Internazionale Crocevia
Via Ferraironi 88/G
I-00172 Roma
Tel: (39-6) 241 39 76
Fax: (39-6) 242 41 77

Crocevia is a development agency supporting rural development projects in the Third World and also dedicated to information and awareness raising in Italy. Grassroots genetic resources conservation to strengthen peasant agriculture is a fundamental and long-time concern of this organisation. They support a range of on-farm conservation and breeding projects in the South, and also work actively for local genetic resources management and a sound national policy in Italy.

### Netherlands

*National Coordinator*
Dr Jaap Hardon
CGN (CPRO-DLO)
Postbus 16
NL-6700 AA Wageningen
Tel: (31-8370) 77075
Fax: (31-8370) 16513

As Director of the Netherlands national genebank, Dr Hardon is keen on developing a more integrated national programme involving NGOs and local groups. He is currently talking with NGOs about offering back-up space in his genebank and land in Wageningen to grow out amateur collections and involve them in research.

*NGOs*
Mr A.J.F. Lieberwerth
Het Hof van Eden
Postbus 636
NL-3500 AP Utrecht
Tel: (31-30) 31 92 00

'The Court of Eden' houses the largest private collection of plant genetic resources in the Netherlands with over 30,000 accessions of all crops from all over the world, including Tibet, the Andes (range of tubers), Ethiopia (Teff), etc. Eight staff in total grow out 12–18,000 accessions a year on small plots outside Utrecht, among small farmers to avoid cross pollination. They hold an open day every Saturday for the public.

De Kleine Aarde
Postbus 151
NL-5280 AD Boxtel
Tel: (31-4116) 84921

'The Small Earth' is an environmental organisation working for the past 20 years on sustainable agriculture and environmental issues. They carry out a range of projects to promote ecological farming. Part of their work focuses on the use of local varieties suitable for such agricultural systems.

## Nordic region

Dr Stig Blixt
Director
Nordic Gene Bank
PO Box 41
S-230 53 Alnarp
Tel: (46-40) 46 17 90
Fax: (46-40) 46 21 88

The Nordic Gene Bank carries out a collective conservation programme for Denmark, Finland, Iceland, Norway and Sweden, devoted specifically to crops developed in Scandinavia.

## Norway

*National Coordinator*
Mr Arne Wold
Statens Frokontroll
PO Box 68
N-1432 As-NLH
Tel: (47-9) 94 95 32
Fax: (47-9) 94 95 67

*NGOs*
Jan Erik Mælam
Norsk Senter for økologisk Landbruk

Tingvoll
Tel: (47-73) 31342

The Norwegian Centre for Ecologically Sound Agriculture is working on conservation and use of traditional crops and can be contacted for further information about the work of the informal sector in Norway.

Anne Karin Hufthammer
Norsk Bufe
Zoologisk Museum
Museplass 3
N-5014 Bergen University

The aims of this organisation are to protect old breeds of farm animals, increase the understanding of rustic breeds for the development of sustainable agriculture and act as a focal point for groups and individuals concerned with animal genetic resources conservation.

## Poland

### National Coordinator
Prof. H.J. Czembor
Plant Breeding & Acclimatisation Institute (IHAR)
Radzikow near Warsaw
05-870 Blonie
Tel: (48-22) 55 26 11
Fax: (48-22) 55 47 14

### NGOs
Mr Wackaw Swiecicki
Individual Farmers Solidarity Union
Country Commission for Ecology, Health & Social Affairs
Smocza 11-4
01-056 Warsaw
Tel: (48-2) 26 98 10
Fax: (48-2) 26 35 48

Wackaw is working to promote ecological farming in Poland in liaison with Solidarity and IFOAM. He can be contacted for further information about local genetic resources work in Poland.

## Portugal

*National Coordinator*
Dr Miguel Mota
Dept. of Genetic and Breeding
Estaçao Agronómica Nacional
P-2780 Oeiras
Tel: (351-1) 443 04 42
Fax: (351-1) 442 08 67

*NGOs*
Mr Manuel Rodrigues
Confederaçao National da Agricultura
Rua Visconde da Luz, 45-4
Apartado 253
P-3000 Coimbra
Tel: (351-39) 3305
Fax: (351-39) 38649

CNA is working to safeguard and strengthen the bio- and cultural diversity of communally- administered wooded areas in the highlands of Portugal. These zones and their traditional farming systems are under threat from the spread of industrial eucalyptus production, which is undermining the genetic diversity and scope for rural development in the mountains of Portugal.

## Russia

*National Coordinator*
Mr Sergei Alexanian
VIR
42-44 Herzen Street
190000 Leningrad
Tel: (314) 4848
Fax: (311) 8762

*NGOs*
Mr Sviatoslave Zublin
Coordinator
Socio-Ecological Union
Krasmoarmeiskaya 25, 85
125310 Moscow

The Socio-Ecological Union is active in a range of problems facing

Russian agriculture, health and environment. They are interested in issues related to biodiversity and should be contacted for further information.

### Spain

*National Coordinator*
Dr Rafael Ponz
Banco del Germoplasma, INIA
Apartado 127
Finco 'El Encin'
Alcala de Henares (Madrid)
Tel: (34-1) 881 92 86
Fax: (34-1) 881 92 87

The Spanish national programme is interested in developing cooperative links with NGOs, particularly in helping to grow out their centralised collection, exchanging materials and raising awareness about genetic diversity.

*NGOs*
Mr Bartolomé Martí
Coordinadora de Agricultura Ecológica
Avinguda València 37
E-08750 Molins de Rei (Barcelona)
Tel: (34-3) 668 71 26
Fax: (34-3) 268 01 39

Within its activities to promote alternative agriculture in Spain, CAE coordinates a network of seed savers – farmers and gardeners – who maintain in production and exchange among themselves traditional varieties of horticultural and agricultural crops. A full listing of members of the network can be requested from CAE. Their regular newsletter *Ecoagricultura* provides information on sustainable agriculture and genetic resources.

Mr Francisco Garcia
CEIDER
Pascual y Genís 21, pta. 10ª
E-46002 València
Tel: (34-3) 391 31 92
Fax: (34-3) 394 06 61

CEIDER has been working for many years on policy, research and public awareness related to genetic resources and sustainable agriculture. They liaise with a broad range of farmers' organisations, public research institute and professional bodies throughout Spain and hope to stimulate better networking on grassroots conservation and policy discussions. CEIDER publishes *Semillas*, a regular newsletter on genetic resources and biotechnology.

### Sweden

*National Coordinator*
Prof. Lennart Kåhre
Swedish University of Agricultural Sciences
Box 7042
S-750 07 Uppsala
Tel: (46-18) 17 10 00

*NGOs*
Mr Thomas Levander
SESAM
Upplandsgatan 56
S-113 28 Stockholm
Tel: (46-8) 763 20 30 (work) or 31 78 04 (home)

SESAM is a voluntary organisation with over 200 members collecting and preserving vegetables and cereals typical of Scandinavia. Experienced seed savers receive a commission. Samples of all varieties are backed-up through long-term seed storage. SESAM is interested in linking up with other networks active in Europe to exchange experiences.

### Switzerland

*National Coordinator*
Dr Gert Kleijer
Station Fédérale de la Recherche Agronomique de Changins
Route de Duillier
CH-1260 Nyon
Tel: (41-22) 363 47 22
Fax: (41-22) 362 13 25

The Swiss genebank liaises with NGOs and encourages cooperation both at the practical level and through the Swiss National Commission on Plant Genetic Resources.

*NGOs*
Mr Hans-Peter Grünenfelder
Pro Specie Rara
Schneebergstrasse 17
CH-9000 St Gallen
Tel: (41-71) 22 74 20
Fax: (41-71) 22 74 40

PSR is a private foundation established in 1982 and funded by shares, patronage and donations. They carry out extensive activity in livestock whereby animals are bought and maintained on 400 farms. Plant genetic resources work is limited to plants adapted to high altitude: potatoes, pulses, cereals. Small regional fruit orchards to provide grafting material. Some 250 farms are involved in their plant conservation efforts throughout Switzerland. PSR has an office in Czechoslovakia and the former Yugoslavia to coordinate emergency rescue operations of threatened rare farm breeds and is trying to set up a European-wide fund to further support this work.

Mr Karl Stole
Fructus
Waisenhausstr. 4
CH-8820 Wadenswill
Tel: (41-1) 780 43 69

Fructus is a large membership organisation devoted solely to the conservation of traditional Swiss fruit stocks involving amateurs, gardeners and farmers.

### Turkey

*National Coordinator*
The Directorate
Aegean Agricultural Research Institute
PO Box 9
35661 Menemen-Izmir
Tel: (90-542) 11552
Fax: (90-542) 12792

*NGOs*
Ms Ayse Gozen
Sarenceby Yokusu

18-c/11 Besiktas
Tel: (90-1) 261 95 58

Ayse is keen on developing NGO work on genetic resources in Turkey. The organisational base of these activities is very weak right now and funds are lacking for community projects. Ayse can be contacted for further information on Turkish NGO work and perspectives.

### United Kingdom

*National Coordinator*
Mr J.C. Suich
Head of Research Policy Coordination Division
Ministry of Agriculture, Fisheries & Food (MAFF)
Nobel House
17 Smith Square
London SW1P 3JR
Tel: (44-71) 238 56 13
Fax: (44-71) 238 55 97

The UK houses a range of genetic resources collections dealing with vegetables, dryland crops, beans, forages, wild species and fruits. Some of them are supportive of the work of NGOs in this field. A national committee and programme is in the process of formalisation. The University of Birmingham is trying to develop a curriculum for training in grassroots conservation of plant genetic resources.

*NGOs*
Dr Jeremy Cherfas
Genetic Resources Department
Henry Doubleday Research Association
Ryton on Dunsmore
Coventry CV8 3LG
Tel: (44-273) 30 35 17
Fax: (44-273) 63 92 29

Within its activities to promote organic gardening and farming, HDRA runs a Seed Heritage Programme and coordinates a network of 40 Seed Guardians who save and grow out materials for national exchange. In 1991, rejuvenation of HDRA's collection of 200 varieties commenced at Ryton Gardens and publication of a quarterly newsletter for seed savers, called *Leaflet*, began. Other recent publications include *The Vegetable Finder*, a full listing of all open-pollinated (non-hybrid)

**180**

vegetable varieties available on the UK market. Those only supplied by one maintainer – a full 60 per cent! – are marked by a symbol to indicate that they are particularly threatened with extinction from British gardens. HDRA engages in a wide range of public awareness raising activities on genetic erosion and is taking an active role to help stimulate networking among grassroots conservation groups throughout Europe.

Mr Matt Dunwell
The Wayward Trust
Ragman's Lane Farm
Lower Lydbrook
Gloucestershire GL17 9PA
Tel: (44-594) 86 02 44
Fax: (44-594) 86 01 23

The Wayward Trust is a small charity organisation interested in projects that contribute to grassroots conservation of biological diversity in Europe. They have supported a range of British NGOs in this field and are interested in reaching out to other associations in the rest of Europe.

## (Former) Yugoslavia

*National Coordinator*
Dr Milutin Pencic
Federal Secretariat for Development
Omladinskih Grigada 1
11070 Novi Beograd
Tel: (38-11) 19 01 11
Fax: (38-11) 222 29 09

## International level

FAO
Via delle Terme di Caracalla
I-00100 Rome
ITALY
Contacts: Director, Regional Office for Europe
Dr José Esquinas-Alcázar, Commission on Plant Genetic Resources

The UN Food and Agriculture Organisation is involved in genetic resources conservation (crop, forest, animal and aquatic), mostly through direct support to national programmes, particularly in the developing countries. FAO's regional European office supports research and networking on a range of crops. FAO's Commission on Plant Genetic Resources is an intergovernmental body responsible for policy issues affecting genetic resources.

GRAIN
Jonqueres 16, 6º D
E-08003 Barcelona
SPAIN
Tel: (34-3) 310 59 09
Fax: (34-3) 310 59 52
Contacts: Mr Henk Hobbelink, Coordinator
Ms Renée Vellvé, Programme Officer

GRAIN works at the research, information, NGO networking and policy level to promote people's control over genetic resources for sustainable development, North and South. Through its special project on conservation in Europe, GRAIN is active in raising awareness, lobbying and networking to strengthen the role of grassroots organisations in the management of Europe's genetic heritage, particularly within local and regional development strategies.

IBPGR
Via delle Sette Chiese, 142
I-00145 Rome
ITALY
Tel: (39-6) 574 47 19
Fax: (39-6) 575 03 09
Contact:  Dr Emile Frison, European Regional Officer

IBPGR, soon to become the International Plant Genetic Resources Institute (IPGRI), promotes national genebank programmes throughout the world. It is increasingly interested in the work of NGOs and local organisations in genetic resources conservation and use. IBPGR supports collecting missions, research, conservation activities and information work. Its programme in Europe aims to assure support to conservation work particularly in Eastern Europe.

RAFI
130 Slater Street, Suite 750
Ottawa, Ontario K1P 6E2

182

CANADA
Tel: (1-613) 565 09 00
Fax: (1-613) 594 87 05
Contact: Mr Pat Mooney, Director

The Rural Advancement Foundation International works to support grassroots conservation work through research, policy work, lobbying and networking on a global scale. They have produced many publications on the conservation crisis and the role of local organisations and support regional programmes in the developing countries.

Seed Savers Exchange
Rural Route 3
PO Box 239
Decorah, IA 52101
USA
Contact: Mr Kent Whealy, Director

The Seed Savers Exchange is probably the largest grassroots conservation network in the world, focusing on plants. Although it is an American organisation, it does have foreign membership. The SSE's *1992 Annual Yearbook*, which is a catalogue of varieties being maintained for exchange and addresses of the suppliers, lists about 20 participants from Europe, East and West. SSE provides a range of services to its membership, including publications, meetings and research.

WWF International
Avenue du Mont-Blanc
CH-1196 Gland
SWITZERLAND
Tel: (41-22) 364 95 26
Fax: (41-22) 364 82 19
Contact: Dr Michel Pimbert, Head, Biodiversity Programme

The World Wide Fund for Nature supports *in situ* conservation programmes throughout the world and produces many publications on the threats to the environment. The Biodiversity Programme focuses on policy issues, project work and awareness raising on the many facets of biodiversity conservation. Projects in the pipeline, in conjunction with the European Programme, include a video on grassroots conservation of genetic resources in Europe and support to local organisations.

# Annex 3: Selected reading

## Books and reports

Ashworth, Suzanne, *Seed to Seed: Seed saving techniques for the vegetable gardener*, Seed Savers Exchange, Decorah, 1991.

> A practical, hands-on guidebook to saving seeds of traditional vegetable crops, mostly of temperate climates. Alongside general tips for the backyard seed saver, provides a crop-by-crop guide on the history and biology of our common vegetables, how to grow each plant to seed, and special techniques for harvesting and stocking the seeds. Beautifully illustrated and a straightforward text covering 160 garden plants.

Available from Seed Savers Exchange, Rural Route 3, Box 239, Decorah, IA 52101, USA. (A German translation of this work is being prepared by Arche Noah. See Annex 2.)

Beau, Christophe, *Pour que vive la diversité*, PAGE PACA, La Thomassine, 1990.

> PAGE PACA's 'white book' tracing the first six years of southeast France's regional programme on conservation and use of local genetic diversity. From sector to sector – medicinal plants, fruits, forages, bees, goats – the book documents a range of activities undertaken by local NGOs and scientists to collect, research, maintain and utilise traditional plants and animals to diversify local agriculture and create new markets, jobs and public awareness.

Available from PAGE PACA, La Thomassine, F-04100 Manosque, France.

Bommer, D.F.R. and Kay Beese, *Pflanzengenetische Ressourcen: Ein Konzept zur Erhaltung und Nutzung für die Bundesrepublik Deutsch-*

*land*, Schriftenreihe des BMELF, Heft 388, Münster-Hilstrup, Braunschweig, 1990.

A proposal for a German national programme on genetic resources conservation and use, in an international perspective.

Bonjean, Alain and Emmanuel Picard, *Les céréales à paille: origine, histoire, économie, sélection*, Softword/Groupe ITM, 1990.

An illustrated journey through the history of small grain cereals in Europe, especially France, and their current status in agriculture. Looks at how these major crops (barley, wheat, rye, oats, rice and triticale) were introduced and diversified in Europe, the development of plant breeding and the challenges facing breeders today. Provides technical, economic and historic data, with resumes in English.

Brown, A. H. D., et al., *The Use of Plant Genetic Resources*, Cambridge University Press, Cambridge, 1989.

A clear and accessible book on the problems and challenges facing *ex situ* conservation of plant genetic resources. Looks at whether and how genebank collections are being used by breeders, discusses different strategies for managing the collections, looks at the value of wild species for breeding and explains how novel techniques in biotechnology could help in the conservation and use of collections. One chapter focuses on cereals in Europe.

Bundesverband Deutscher Pflanzenzüchter (ed.), *Landwirtschaftliche Pflanzenzuchtung in Deutschland*, Geschichte, Gegenwart und Ausblick, Gelsenkirchen, 1987.

Bureau des Ressources Génétiques (ed.), *La diversité des plantes légumières: hier, aujourd'hui et demain*, JATBA, Paris, 1986.

The proceedings of a French symposium on vegetable genetic diversity: where our crops come from, how they are being managed, the laws affecting the seed supply, and who is doing what to conserve and use crop genetic diversity for horticulture and gardening. Contains a lot of historical information and views from different sectors, from public research to grassroots seed savers.

Available from Technique & Documentation, Lavoisier, 11 rue Lavoisier, F-75384 Paris cedex 08, France.

Chevallier, Daniel, rapporteur, *Rapport sur les applications des biotechnologies à l'agriculture et à l'industrie agro-alimentaire* (Tome II, Annexes), Office Parlementaire d'évaluation et des choix scientifiques, Paris, 1990.

This is a collection of commissioned works for the French Parliament on biotechnology and the food system. Papers include master works by legal experts, economists, journalists and others on a range of issues affecting genetic diversity: the push for patent laws, the transformation of the biotech industry, an overview of current conservation efforts.

Available from Jean-Pierre Gousseau, Assemblé Nationale, 233 boulevard Saint-Germain, F-75355 Paris, France.

Duenbostel, J., *Zum Beispiel Saatgut*, Göttingen, 1990.

A simple and general introduction to plant genetic resources.

Ford-Lloyd, Brian and Michael Jackson, *Plant Genetic Resources: An introduction to their conservation and use*, Edward Arnold, London, 1986.

A compact introduction to genetic resources conservation, as seen from the perspective of the formal sector. Explains the history of crop evolution, conservation strategies and the use of plant genetic resources for breeding. Gives a theoretical and practical overview of the current genebank approach.

Fowler, Cary and Pat Mooney, *Shattering: Food, politics and the loss of genetic diversity*, University of Arizona Press, Tucson, 1990.

A monumental trip through the birth and decline of genetic diversity at the global level. Fowler and Mooney take us into the personalities and politics of genetic erosion and who is doing what about it in international, national and local circles. Some data on Europe, but mostly focused on the developing countries.

Hardon, Jaap, et al., *Common Framework for an Integrated EC Programme on the Conservation of Plant Genetic Resources*, GRAIN, Barcelona, February 1992.

A report drawn up for the EC's plant genetic resources community by a national programme (CGN, the Dutch genebank), and NGO

(GRAIN) and the CGIAR (IBPGR), responding to the European Parliament's initiative to launch an all new programme for genetic resources conservation. The report outlines the history of the Parliament's initiative, an overview of current actitivites, identifies gaps and needs and forwards proposals for setting up the new programme. Stress is put on the need to integrate and equally support the work of genebanks and grassroots organisations in Europe. The report is meant to feed into the disussions on the future of genetic resources conservation and use in Europe.

Available from GRAIN, Jonqueres 16, 6º D, E-08003 Barcelona, Spain.

Keystone Center (ed.), *Keystone International Dialogue Series on Plant Genetic Resources: Oslo Plenary Session (Final Consensus Report)*, GRCS Inc., Washington DC, 1991.

The final outcome of three years of off-the-record consensus-reaching among the main actors in the worldwide debate over control and conservation of plant genetic resources. The Keystone process brought together high-level representatives of industry, government and NGOs to reach agreement on main issues facing management of genetic resources at the global. The final report provides a blueprint for action involving both formal sector scientists and community organisations.

Available from the Keystone Center, P.O. Box 606, Keystone, CO 80435, USA in English, French, Spanish and Portuguese.

Marchenay, Philippe, *A la recherche des variétés locales des plantes cultivées*, PAGE PACA, Hyères, 1987.

A pioneering work of an ethnobotanist taking us into the history and current reality of genetic erosion at the local level in France and how to go about the practicalities of grassroots conservation. A simple but scientifically sound guidebook to collecting and conserving plants at the community level, with a strong emphasis on the importance of local knowledge. Comes with a pocket size practical guide for taking into the field.

Available from PAGE PACA, La Thomassine, F-04100 Manosque, France.

McGloughin, Patricia and Bruno Schmitz (ed.), *Biological Diversity: A challenge to science, the economy and society,* Commission of the European Communities, Brussels.

This is the report of a meeting sponsored by the Commission of the European Communities held in Dublin on 4-6 March 1987. The papers cover all aspects of biodiversity management, with a fair focus on Europe, and conclude with recommendations for action to the EC.

Available from Bruno Schmitz, SAST Unit, DG-XII, Commission of the European Communities, 200 rue de la Loi, B-1049 Brussels, Belgium.

Melandri, Giovanna e Giulio Conte (coordinators), *Ambiente Italia 1992,* Lega per l'Ambiente, Roma, 1992.

A collective work published by the Italian environmental group Lega per l'Ambiente and entirely devoted to biological diversity. A very wide range of contributions look at different issues: genetic erosion, conservation activities by the formal and informal sectors, the need to raise awareness and the elements of an Italian policy framework on managing biodiversity.

Available from Lega per l'Ambiente, Via Salaria 280, I-00199 Rome, Italy.

Recchia, Elena e Alessandra Parente, *La Diversità Biologica in Agricoltura, Zootecnia e in Alimentazione,* WWF Italia, 1991.

A concise and simple educational booklet produced by WWF-Italy for school programmes, NGOs and associations who want to take on the challenge of raising awareness about the importance of biological divesity in the general public. The authors, working with the Gruppo di Attenzione sulle Biotechnologie, take a method-ological approach, providing a tool for teaching about, step by step, the different aspects of genetic erosion, industrialisation of agriculture and conservation strategies.

Available from WWF Italia, Via Salaria 290, I-00199 Rome, Italy.

Regione Toscana, Giunta Regionale, *Un Seme, Un Ambiente: Ricerca di germoplasma di specie erbacee di interesse agricolo in Toscana,* Dipartimento Agricoltura e Foreste, Regione Toscana, Firenze, Dicembre 1991.

A report of the first results of a regional programme to collect and conserve local plant genetic resources in Tuscany. The programme involves the regional government and the agronomists' cooperative Il Bigallo Verde. The booklet reports on initial collecting missions, with a focus not just on seeds but on the farmers and gardeners from whom they were collected and the structural changes facing Tuscan agriculture and its traditional diversity. Available from Giunta Regionale Toscana, Ufficio Pubblicazioni, Centro Stampa, Via di Novoli 26, I-50127 Firenze, Italy.

Seed Savers Exchange (ed.), *Seed Savers 1991 Harvest Edition*, SSE, Decorah, 1991.

This edition of the SSE's harvest publication reports on many events and the general situation with respect to conserving genetic diversity in Europe. A range of reports from NGOs and journalists feature the crisis facing both genebanks, such as the Gatersleben genebank in former East Germany, and grassroots movements, in both the East and the West.

Available from Seed Savers Exchange, Rural Route 3, Box 239, Decorah, IA 52101, USA.

Stubbe, H., *Geschichte des Instituts fur Kulturpflanzenforschung Gatersleben der Deutschenb Akademie der Wissenschaften su Berlin 1943-1968*, Berlin.

van Hintum, Th J. L., et al. (ed.), *Crop Networks: Searching for new concepts for collaborative genetic resources management*, IBPGR, Rome, 1991.

Presents the papers delivered to a meeting held in Wageningen in December 1990 on collaboration among genetic resources programmes in Europe, East and West. Different genebank leaders report on achievements and difficulties in their countries and look at areas for cooperation.

Available from IBPGR, Via delle Sette Chiese 142, I-00145 Rome, Italy.

Zeven, A. C. and A.M. van Harten (ed.), *Broadening the Genetic Base of Crops*, PUDOC, Wageningen, 1979.

The proceedings of a conference held in Wageningen with a range of genetic resources experts looking heavily at the situation in European genetic erosion and current conservation and breeding activities. A bit outdated, but still a useful and interesting source of information about formal genetic resources activities in Europe.

## Periodicals

*Diversity*, GRCS (Washington, DC).

A regular magazine on plant genetic resources for a worldwide audience. Funded by mainly corporate sponsors, it provides wide coverage of new issues in plant genetic resources management, both national programmes and (increasingly) NGO activities. Aside from news pieces there are background reports, commentaries on emerging or controversial issues in genetic resources circles, book reviews and upcoming events.

Diversity: 727 8th Street N.W., Washington, DC 20003, USA.

*Geneflow*, IBPGR (Rome).

A popular magazine put out by the International Board for Plant Genetic Resources. It gives brief news on genetic resources conservation (increasingly including grassroots actions) and reports on specific themes, regions or events. The 1990 issue carries a special and very good section on genetic resources activities, at the official level, in Eastern Europe.

IBPGR: Via delle Sette Chiese 142, I-00145 Rome, Italy. (One issue per year.)

*GRACE*, Kluwer Academic Publishers (Dordrecht).

The former plant genetic resources journal *Die Kulturpflanze*, traditionally produced in Berlin under the direction of the East German genebank at Gatersleben, is being resuscitated under the name *GRACE*, for Genetic Resources And Crop Evolution, and published in the Netherlands.

Kluwer Academic Publishers, PO Box 17, NL-3300 AA Dordrecht, The Netherlands.

*Leaflet*, HDRA (Coventry).

Both a practical and news oriented newsletter for Europe's grassroots seed saving community. It is published quarterly for members of HDRA's Heritage Seed Programme and provides profiles of local initiatives, seed saving tips, lost and found, news from Brussels, and background reports on issues and structures affecting local management of genetic diversity.

HDRA: Genetic Resources Department, National Centre for Organic Gardening, Ryton on Dunsmore, Coventry CV8 3LG, UK.

*Plant Genetic Resources Newsletter*, FAO/IBPGR (Rome).

An international newsletter for the scientific community providing brief progress reports on collecting missions and conservation research all over the world. Most articles in English with resumes in French and Spanish.

IBPGR: Via delle Sette Chiese 142, I-00145 Rome, Italy.

*Sauve qui peut! (Sauve qui veut)*, INRA (Paris).

A new initiative from the public sector in France, *Sauve qui peut!* is a newsletter devoted just to genetic resources. Well written and very informative, it presents special dossiers on crops or programmes, reports of meetings, literature reviews and news from genetic resources circles.

INRA: Cellule de l'Environnement, 147 rue de l'Université, F-75338 Paris cedex 07, France.

*Seedling*, GRAIN (Barcelona).

GRAIN's regular newsletter on genetic resources and biotechnology. Provides regular, up-to-date information on the seed industry, biotechnology, international debates, grassroots conservation initiatives, news from the network, literature reviews and upcoming events. Free for NGOs, US$ 35 per year all others.

GRAIN: Jonqueres 16, 6ºD, E-08003 Barcelona, Spain. (4-5 issues per year.)

*Semillas*, CEIDER/SECODES/GRAIN (València).

The Spanish language edition of *Seedling*, produced in cooperation between CEIDER, SECODES and GRAIN.

## SAVING THE SEED

CEIDER: Pascaul y Génis 21, pta 10ª, E-46002 València, Spain.

*SemiRaris*, PAGE PACA (Manosque).

The magazine of the PAGE PACA regional programme for genetic conservation in southeast France. It contains background articles on on-farm/in-garden conservation, news from the members of the programme, a rare seed exchange platform and reviews of the status of indigenous crops. Volume 3-4 is a special double issue providing a catalogue of rare plants available to amateurs from specialised nurseries, amateurs, associations and seed companies dedicated to old crops.

PAGE PACA: La Thomassine, F-04100 Manosque, France. (Two issues per year.)

# Notes

**Chapter 1**

1    *Seed to Seed*, Seed Savers Exchange, Decorah, p. 13.
2    A.C. Zeven and J.M.J. de Wet, *Dictionary of cultivated plants and their regions of diversity*, PUDOC, Wageningen, 1982, p. 16.
3    Ibid., p. 149.
4    Cary Fowler and Pat Mooney, *Shattering: Food, Politics and the Loss of Genetic Diversity*, Arizona Press, 1990, p. 11
5    Alain Bonjean and Emmanuel Picard, *Les céréales à paille: origine, histoire, économie, sélection*, Softword/Groupe ITM, 1990, pp. 60-61.
6    J.G. Hawkes, *The diversity of crop plants*, Harvard University Press, Cambridge, 1983, p.10.
7    Quoted in A.C. Zeven and J.M.J. de Wet, op. cit., p. 21.
8    D.F.R. Bommer, 'The historical development of international collaboration in plant genetic resources', in *Crop networks: Searching for new concepts for collaborative genetic resources management*, IBPGR, Rome, 1991, p. 3.
9    Emmer is an ancient form of wheat, from which modern types were later developed.
10   A.C. Zeven and J.M.J. de Wet, op cit., p. 160.
11   Like emmer, spelt is an ancient form of wheat once widely grown throughout Europe.
12   The stone fruit family includes those fruit with a hard 'pit' inside: cherry, apricot, plum, almond, damson, peach, etc.
13   Jules Pretty, 'Sustainable Agriculture in the Middle Ages: the English Manor', in *The Agricultural History Review*, Vol. 38, British Agricultural History Society, University of Leeds, West Yorkshire, 1990, p. 5.
14   Alain Bonjean and Emmanuel Picard, op. cit, pp. 75–6.
15   Phillipe Marchenay, 'Les aspects ethnobotaniques de la diversité variétale: application à la prospection des variétés traditionelles', in *La diversité des plantes légumières: hier, aujourd'hui et demain*, JATBA, Paris, 1986, pp. 130–1.

16  Jules Pretty, 'Farmers' Extension Practice and Technology Adapta-
    tion: Agricultural Reveolution in 17th–19th Century Britain', in
    *Agriculture and Human Values*, Vol. VIII, Numbers 1 and 2,
    Agriculture, Food and Human Values Society, University of Florida,
    Gainesville, Winter–Spring 1991, p. 142.

17  C. Populer, Director of the Plant Pathology Station in Gembloux,
    Report to the Director General of the Agricultural Research
    Administration, Ministry of Agriculture, concerning the impact of
    new biotechnologies on plant genetic diversity with reference to
    request for information of 11.06.90 addressed to ARA from
    GRAIN.

18  Philippe Marchenay, *A la recherche des variétiés des plantes cultivées*,
    PAGE PACA, La Thomassine, 1987, p. 46.

19  *Encyclopedia of Wild Edible Plants*, six volumes under preparation,
    Editions Debard, Paris.

20  Jules Pretty, 'Sustainable Agriculture in the Middle Ages: The
    English Manor'. op.cit., p. 14.

21  Cary Fowler and Pat Mooney, op. cit., p. 218.

*Chapter 2*

1  Christopher Beau, *Pour que vive la diversité*, PAGE PACA,
   Manosque, 1990, p. 25.

2  Data, represented in graph, from Erna Bennett, 'Wheats of the
   Mediterranean Basin', in *Survey of Crop Genetic Resources in their
   Centres of Diversity*, O. Frankel (editor), FAO/IBP, Rome, 1973,
   p. 3.

3  'Another day older and deeper in debt: the politics of industrial
   agriculture', *The Ecologist*, April 1992, p. 49.

4  Alain Bonjean and Emmanuel Picard, *Les céréales à paille: origine,
   histoire, économie, sélection*, Softward Groupe ITM 1990, pp. 96–7.

5  Roland Petit-Pigeard, in a talk given at the farmers' seminar
   'Orientation et financement de la recherche sur les semences', report
   published by FADEAR, Paris, 1991, p. 4.

6  Pat Roy Mooney, 'The Law of the Seed', *Development Dialogue*,
   1983:1–2, Dag Hammarskjöld Foundation, Uppsala, p. 96.

7  John Duesing, in a conversation with Renée Vellvé of GRAIN in
   Barcelona, 30 January 1992.

8  J. Koenig et al., 'Cereals genetic resources networks in France', in
   *Crop networks: searching for new concepts for collaborative genetic
   resources management*, IBPGR, Rome 1991, p. 111.

9  In a letter addressed to Renée Vellvé of GRAIN, dated 13 October 1990.

10  G. Fischbeck, 'Evaluation of cereals in Europe', in Brown et al., *The use of plant genetic resources*, Cambridge University Press, 1989, pp. 197–211.

11  Peter Day, 'Problems and opportunities confronting the exploitation of genetic diversity', in *Biological diversity: a challenge to science, the economy and society*, Patricia McGloughlin and Bruno Schmitz (editors), unpublished proceedings of a European Conference, Dublin, 4–6 March 1987, p. 27.

12  A.C. Zeven, 'Collecting genetic resources in highly industrialised Europe, especially the Netherlands' in *Broadening the genetic base of crops*, PUDOC, Wageningen, 1979, p. 50.

13  Michael Flitner, in a letter to Renée Véllvé of GRAIN dated 9 June 1992.

14  A.C. Zeven, op. cit., p. 52.

15  In a letter to Renée Vellvé of GRAIN dated 27 June 1990.

16  François Haquin, 'Qualité des blés françaises: le choix variétal va évoluer' in *Semences et progrès*, No. 63, April–May–June 1990, Paris, p. 9.

17  In a letter to Renée Vellvé of GRAIN dated 8 September 1990.

18  In a letter to Renée Vellvé of GRAIN dated 3 July 1990.

19  In a letter to Renée Vellvé of GRAIN dated 24 July 1990.

20  In a letter to Renée Vellvé of GRAIN dated 8 August 1990.

21  The *IBPGR/FAO Plant Genetic Resources Newsletter*, published by FAO in Rome, reports regularly on such missions.

22  Karl Hammer, et al., 'Collection of plant genetic resources in South Italy, 1986', in *Die Kulturpflanze*, volume 35, Berlin, 1987, pp. 389–399.

23  Christian Lehmann, 'Genetic Resources', in *Die Kulturpflanze*, Volume 36, Berlin, 1988, pp. 71–83.

24  W. Hondelmann, 'Safeguarding germplasm of medical and aromatic plants in the Federal Republic of Germany', in *FAO/IBPGR Plant Genetic Resources Newsletter*, Number 78/79, FAO, Rome, pp. 1–3.

25  In a letter to Renée Vellvé of GRAIN dated 2 August 1990.

26  Maria Carmen Alamán et al., 'La recogida de germoplasma por la submeseta de España', in *FAO/IBPGR Plant Genetic Resources Newsletter*, Number 54, FAO, Rome, 1983, pp. 11–13.

27  Data calculated from 'Beschrijvende Rassenlijst voor Landbouwgewassen', Wageningen, 1990.

28   Y. Hervé, 'Evolution des crucifères cultivées et preservation des ressources génétiques en France', source unknown.

29   A.C. Zeven and J.M.J. de Wet, *Dictionary of cultivated plants and their centres of diversity*, Pudoc, Wageningen, 1982, p. 114.

30   W.A. Cowling, 'Collection of wild *Lupinus* in Greece', in *FAO/IBPGR Plant Genetic Resources Newsletter*, Number 65, FAO, Rome, pp. 20–22.

31   L.M. Martin et al., 'Recogida y evaluación del género *Lupinus* en España' in *FAO/IBPGR Plant Genetic Resources Newsletter*, Number 63, FAO, Rome, pp. 41–42.

32   Figure provided by Jeremy Cherfas of HDRA in a letter to Renée Vellvé of GRAIN dated 23 June 1992.

33   Quoted in Jack Hawkes, *The Diversity of Crop Plants*, Harvard University Press, 1983, p. 100.

34   Pat Mooney, op. cit., p. 115.

35   For an overview of how it will affect farmers, consumers, plant breeders, genebanks and the Third World, see an earlier GRAIN publication, *Patenting life forms in Europe: Proceedings of an international conference held at the European Parliament, 7–8 February 1989*, ICDA Seeds Campaign, Barcelona, March 1989.

### Chapter 3

1   Final Consensus Report, Oslo Plenary Session, Keystone Centre, 1991, p. 6.

2   Quoted in Donald Plucknett, et al., *Genebanks and the world's food*, Princeton University Press, Princeton, 1987, p. 16.

3   Christian O. Lehmann, 'Genetic Resources', in *Die Kulturpflanze*, Vol. 36, Berlin, 1988, p. 73.

4   Idem.

5   Cary Fowler and Pat Mooney, *Shattering: Food, politics and the loss of genetic diversity*, University of Arizona Press, Tucson, 1990, pp. 149–54.

6   Data compiled from IBPGR's *Annual Report 1981*, IBPGR, Rome, pp. 103-8.

7   Pat Roy Mooney, 'The Law of the Seed', *Development Dialogue*, 1983:1–2, Dag Hammarskjöld Foundation, Uppsala, p. 26.

8   Donald Plucknett et al., op. cit., p. 188.

9   D.R.F. Bommer, 'The historical development of international collaboration in plant genetic resources', in *Crop networks: Searching*

*for new concepts for collaborative genetic resources management*, IBPGR, Rome, 1991, p. 9.

10 Daycha Siripatra and Witoon Lianchamroon, 'An integrated NGO approach in Thailand', in *Growing Diversity: Genetic resources and local food security*, GRAIN (ed.), IT Publications, London, 1992, p. 41.

11 Data compiled by GRAIN from IBPGR's databases.

12 V.A. Dragavtsev and S.M. Alexanian, 'The VIR network: problems of mobilisation and conservation of plant genetic resources', in *Crop networks: searching for new concepts for collaborative management of genetic resources*, IBPGR, Rome 1991, p. 67–8.

13 Cary Fowler and Pat Mooney, draft, unfinished work provisionally entitled 'The Laws of Lysenko', started in 1991 and which we hope they finish and publish someday!

14 *A Strategy for the International Plant Genetic Resources Institute*, Draft for comment, IPGRI, Rome, December 1991, p. 39.

15 J. Puchalski et al., 'Studies on genetic shift in rye seed after long-term storage in seed bank', in *Crop networks: searching for new concepts for collaborative genetic resources management*, IBPGR, Rome 1991, p. xi.

16 Th. Hazekamp (editor), *CGN Genebank Protocol*, (CPRO-DLO), Wageningen, December 1991, 45 p., provides a technical review of the practices of the Dutch genebank.

17 J.J. Hardon, 'The case for a European Community genetic resources programme', in *The conservation of wild progenitors of cultivated plants*, Proceedings of the colloquy organised by the Council of Europe together with the Israel Nature Reserves Authorities, Strasbourg, 1991, p. 118.

18 D. Stoyanov, Director, on behalf of the staff of the Institute for Plant Genetic Resources in Sadovo, near Plovdiv, in a letter to GRAIN dated 2 June 1992.

19 Renée Vellvé and Michael Flitner, 'East German genebank in limbo', in *Seedling*, Vol. 8, No. 3, GRAIN, Barcelona, July 1991, pp. 6–10.

20 Ministry of Agriculture, Fisheries and Food, *Review of UK policy on the ex-situ conservation of plant genetic resources*, MAFF, London, February 1992.

21 J.J. Hardon, Director of the Centre for Genetic Resources (the Netherlands), 'The need for a common integrated programme on plant genetic resources conservation within the European Community', presentation made to the European Parliament on 19 June 1991.

22  Ministry of Agriculture, Fisheries and Food, *Review of UK policy on the ex-situ conservation of plant genetic resources*, MAFF, London, February 1992.

23  Christian Lehmann, in a letter to Renée Vellvé of GRAIN dated 9 November 1991, two months before his death.

24  IBPGR's database on world genebank holdings, provided to GRAIN, records 3,559,710 accessions in storage as of December 1991.

25  In a letter to Renée Vellvé of GRAIN dated 23 March 1992.

26  In a letter to Renée Vellvé of GRAIN dated 1 October 1990.

27  P.M. Perret, 'Actual and future concepts for collaboration in crop genetic resources', in *Crop networks: Searching for new concepts for collaborative genetic resources management*, IBPGR, Rome, 1991, p. 13.

28  Donald L. Plucknett et al., op. cit., p. 168

29  Z. Bulinska-Radomska, W. Podyma and S. Góral, 'Plant genetic resources conservation programme in Poland: A multi-institutional collaboration', in *Crop networks: Searching for new concepts for collaborative genetic resources management*, IBPGR, Rome, 1991, p. 82.

30  Figures quoted during discussions among the European genebank community gathered for the EUCARPIA/IBPGR symposium on crop networks, Wageningen, December 1990.

31  *FAO Seed Review 1984–1985*, FAO, Rome, 1987, p. 462.

32  Ibid., p. 536.

33  J.J. Hardon, *Crop genetic resources conservation in Western Europe*, Paper presented to the Workshop on opportunities of European cooperation in the conservation of plant genetic resources, Bonn, 28 September 1989, p. 10.

34  *FAO Seed Review 1984–1985*, FAO, Rome, 1987, p. 455.

35  Ibid., p. 506.

36  'Industrial Patents, Plant Breeding and Genetic Resources: A Plant Breeder's View', in *Patenting Life Forms in Europe*, ICDA Seeds Campaign, Barcelona, March 1989, p. 36.

37  Meeting of the EC's Ad Hoc Group of Experts on Crop Genetic Resources, Brussels, 7 March 1991.

*Chapter 4*

1  Speaking at the Seed Savers Exchange Annual Campout Conven-

tion, Iowa, August 1991, in *Seed Savers 1991 Harvest Edition*, SSE, Decorah, 1991, p. 72.

2  Appeal circulated by the Escuela Taller de Cardona at a European-wide meeting on regional development, organised by the Basque farmers organisation EHNE in Zestona, May 1991.

3  André Hatesse, 'Le point de vue des collectionneurs amateurs', in *La diversité des plantes légumières: hier, aujourd'hui et demain*, JATBA, Paris, 1986, p. 203.

4  Blue potatoes come from the Andes, but they were introduced into Provence some two hundred years ago and have become part of the local culture. La Negresse is a typical peasant cultivar of the region and the Provençal people consider it part of their heritage.

5  Jost Ettlin, Swiss biodynamic breeder and observer of the work of Pflanzenzuchtverein Wernstein, in a conversation with Renée Vellvé of GRAIN in Vallvidrera on 12 July 1991.

6  Nancy Arrowsmith et al., *Allgemeine Gemüsefibel: Zasammenstellung der in Österreich kommerzeill-erhältlichen nicht-hybriden und nicht geschützen Gemüsesorten*, Arche Noah, 1991, 159 p.

7  Nancy Arrowsmith, 'Noah's Ark: Seed-Saving Activities in Central Europe', in *Seed Savers 1991 Summer Edition*, SSE, Decorah, 1991, p. 79.

8  Idem.

9  Idem.

10  Nancy Arrowsmith, 'Emergency Appeal for European Seed-Saving Groups', in *Seed Savers 1991 Harvest Edition*, SSE, Decorah, 1991, p. 111.

11  Ibid., p. 112.

12  In the foreword to *The Vegetable Finder*, HDRA, Coventry, 1992.

13  Regione Toscana, Giunta Regionale, *Un seme, un ambiente: Ricerca di germoplasma di specie erbacee di interesse agricolo in Toscana, primeri resultati*, Dipartimento Agricoltura e Foreste, Firenze, 1991, p. 50.

14  Ibid., p. 52.

15  The information for this section is taken from different publications of Pro Specie Rara.

*Chapter 5*

1  'EC agrees shake-up of farm policy', *Financial Times*, London, 22 May 1992.

2   Phillippe Marchenay, *A la recherche des variétés locales de plantes cultivées*, PAGE PACA, 1987.

3   Dr. László Holly, Director of the Research Centre for Agrobotany and Chairman of the National Genebank, in a letter to Renée Vellvé of GRAIN dated 9 April 1992.

4   Idem.

5   Pietro Perrino, et al., 'Valutazione e selezione di farro in ambienti marginali dell'appennino molisano', estratto da *L'informatore Agrario*, Verona, XLVII(42), 1991.

6   J.J. Hardon, et al., *Common Framework for an Integrated EC Programme on the Conservation of Plant Genetic Resources*, GRAIN, February 1992.

7   Mr. D. Dessylas, Head of the Division for Agricultural Research, DG-VI, during a meeting with Renée Vellvé of GRAIN in Brussels on 19 December 1991.

# Index

**206**